Fifty Golden Years
of the Rand

FIFTY
GOLDEN YEARS
OF THE RAND
1886–1936

by
D. JACOBSSON
Mining Editor of
'The Star', Johannesburg

With an Introduction by
THE HON. PATRICK DUNCAN
C.M.G., K.C., LL.D., M.P.
Minister of Mines for
The Union of South Africa

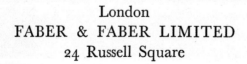

London
FABER & FABER LIMITED
24 Russell Square

FIRST PUBLISHED IN JULY MCMXXXVI
BY FABER AND FABER LIMITED
24 RUSSELL SQUARE LONDON W.C.1
SECOND IMPRESSION JULY MCMXXXVI
PRINTED IN GREAT BRITAIN BY
LATIMER TREND AND CO PLYMOUTH

Written to Commemorate
the Jubilee
of
JOHANNESBURG
and of the
WITWATERSRAND
Gold Mining Industry

Introduction

It is not an exaggeration to say that the phenomenal development of the Witwatersrand, and, with it, the astounding growth of its main centre, Johannesburg, have attracted world-wide attention. Thus it is very appropriate that the fiftieth anniversary of the founding of this newest of cities should be celebrated by an Empire Exhibition during the latter part of this year.

The exhibition will, undoubtedly, attract many thousands of visitors from all parts of the Empire and it is to be expected that they will wish to acquire, in some simple form, sound and reliable information regarding the rise and progress of our gold industry and of its chief city.

Mr. Jacobsson's book, which I am asked to introduce by these lines, will, in my opinion, meet this demand fully and admirably. Its appearance at this moment is therefore well timed.

This book is, however, much more than a brochure or handbook for overseas visitors. It gives an accurate account of the history of our goldfields from the first discovery of gold on the Witwatersrand up to the present highly organized stage of the industry.

Written with a facile pen, the story unfolds many picturesque glimpses of life in the days of the old gold diggers; it portrays the romance of fortunes made by

INTRODUCTION

courageous decisions of men of foresight and enterprise, and it throws into bold relief many of the prominent men who helped to build up this great national industry.

Not the least of its merits is the fact that, whilst touching lightly on controversial matters, the author carefully avoids expressing any partisan views, and explains that he is merely referring to these matters in order to portray the sequence of events and their bearing on the development of the Witwatersrand.

Mr. Jacobsson, who, by virtue of his position as Mining Editor of *The Star* and through his long association with journalism on the Witwatersrand, is eminently fitted to undertake this compilation, has accomplished his task with great skill. The result is a story of great interest, not only to those who seek reliable information regarding our goldfields, but also to those who wish to possess a brief but accurate account of the romantic history of the Witwatersrand.

PATRICK DUNCAN

Foreword

This little work is designed to present in a short compass all the essential aspects of the rise of the Witwatersrand[1] gold mining industry to world pre-eminence and of Johannesburg to a city of world importance.

It makes no pretence to being an adequate history of development and achievement, for to each of these broad subjects many volumes could be devoted. As the gold of the Witwatersrand is found in close association with other valuable minerals, so the mosaic of its story is made up of many patterns. There is the romance of discovery, the heroic work of pioneers and in particular the sacrifice and devotion of brave women, the daring of finance, the conquests of science, and the achievement in control and administration. The story of development has its tragic as well as its romantic side, and a tribute would be due to the heroism of workers, both white and black, in the face of calamities inseparable from the risks of mining. Yet these would not complete the story. There would be a record of spiritual growth, and of civic and cultural advance. Political adventure, the clash of arms, and industrial strife would claim a place in the narrative, and drama and crime could not be neglected in a faithful chronicle.

[1] Ridge of White Waters. So called from the little streams that issued from the hills and showed white in the distance.

FOREWORD

In these pages aspects which may raise points of unprofitable controversy and division are dealt with only in so far as they are necessary to the thread of the story.

The jubilee of the fields is to be commemorated by an Empire Exhibition (September 15th, 1936, to January 15th, 1937), the first to be held outside Great Britain, and while this modest volume may be welcome to exhibition visitors as an introduction to mines and city, it is also hoped that it may be of some little value as a local record.

The popular explanation of many technical features of mining should be helpful to a big class of mining investors unfamiliar with such aspects, which are yet of close importance to them.

The preparation of this survey has necessarily involved much research. A great deal of the technical material is based on scientific publications and papers submitted to scientific societies and these and other sources of reference are gratefully acknowledged at the close of the volume.

Here too will be found statistics of production which provide a striking contrast between the figures of 1932 (the last year under gold standard conditions) and those of the three following years, and show the wide variations in the working results of individual producers.

Also included is a map, specially drawn for this publication, which reveals at a glance the significance of the recent remarkable expansion of the industry.

D. J.

Contents

CONTENTS

CONTENTS

13

CONTENTS

14

Illustrations

15

The Birth Notice of the Rand

The following is a translation of the proclamation that appeared in the Government Gazette (Staats Courant) of the South African Republic on September 8th, 1886:

WHEREAS it appears to the Government of the South African Republic that it is advisable that the farms named Driefontein, Elandsfontein, southern portion Doornfontein, Turffontein, Government farm Randjeslaagte, Langlaagte, Paardekraal, Vogelstruisfontein and Roodepoort, all situate in the Witwatersrand, district Heidelberg, be declared a public digging, Now, therefore, I, STEPHANUS JOHANNES PAULUS KRUGER, State President of the South African Republic, in terms of Article 5 of Law No. 8, 1885, do proclaim the abovementioned farms a Public Digging in the following order and from the following dates respectively, namely:

The farms Driefontein and Elandsfontein on Monday, 20th September, 1886;

The southern portion of the farm Doornfontein and the farm Turffontein on Monday, 27th September, 1886;

The piece of Government ground named Randjeslaagte and the farm named Langlaagte on Monday, 4th October, 1886;

THE BIRTH NOTICE OF THE RAND

The farms named Paardekraal, Vogelstruisfontein and Roodepoort on Monday, 11th October, 1886, in so far as the same have not been beaconed off by owners or lessees for 'Mynpacht-brieven', or according to Article 20 of Law 8, 1885, as reserved cultivated lands, gardens, agricultural lands and water-leadings, in the vicinity thereof.

GOD PRESERVE LAND AND PEOPLE

Given under my hand at the Government Offices at Pretoria, on this, the 8th day of September, A.D. 1886.

(*Sgd.*) S. J. P. KRUGER, State President.
(*Sgd.*) W. EDUARD BOK, State Secretary.

PART ONE

The Broad Outlook
and the Achievement

The Broad Outlook and the Achievement

In the presence of so much restless industry and human activity to-day it is scarcely possible to recapture the isolation and solitude of the Witwatersrand fifty years ago when it yielded a bare sustenance to a few pastoralists many miles away from their nearest markets. Pretoria, then the largest settled community in the Transvaal, was but a village; to-day, warmed by the wealth of the gold mining activity, it enjoys the proud position of the administrative capital of the Union with all the dignity and bearing that such a status confers. In contrast, Kimberley, the diamond city, was then at the height of her prosperity, seemingly mistress through her wealth of her own destiny and the destiny of the subcontinent; to-day she languishes, almost forgotten by a world she once flattered, her treasures for long unmined and unsought.[1] The demand for gold is constant; diamonds reflect the caprice of changing mood and fortune. Yet Kimberley's wealth played a great part in revealing the riches of the Witwatersrand.

In the opening up of South Africa and in the shaping of its history the Witwatersrand gold mining industry has exercised a predominating influence. The situation of the goldfield in the heart of the sub-

[1] There are now welcome signs of a revival of the diamond industry.

continent has been, of course, a factor of first importance, for, so placed, the Witwatersrand has in its own growth and expansion promoted to a marked degree the growth and expansion of South Africa itself. Without the gold mines the progress of the country would probably have been determined mainly by the pace and limits of its agricultural advance, and if the gold mines had been based on the coastline and not far in the hinterland, there would have been little stimulus to internal development.

At the time of the gold discoveries the nearest railheads were Kimberley in the Cape and Ladysmith in Natal, each roughly 300 miles distant by road from the scene. In the whole subcontinent there were not 2000 miles of railway, in which the capital invested was less than £16,000,000. Goods traffic was under 500,000 tons a year, and passenger journeys did not reach 3,000,000. Earnings were about £1,250,000 and working expenditure well under a million. The value of South Africa's imports and exports was less than £13,000,000. To-day railway mileage in South Africa, including South-West Africa, is close on 14,000. The detailed figures for the year 1934-5 showed that capital expenditure had almost reached £170,000,000, goods traffic (apart from live stock) totalled nearly 25,000,000 tons, and passenger journeys were over 83,000,000. Earnings for the year were £29,879,178, and expenditure £25,990,453, showing a surplus of £3,888,725. The value of the Union's imports and exports has risen to roughly £175,000,000.

How mining started on the Witwatersrand: Primitive pioneer plant and shaft head. The ore was carted to mills on water sites often many miles away.

Reproduction by courtesy of The Star, Johannesburg.

No one would be so foolish as to put all this great expansion to the credit of the gold mining industry, but that it has been the mainspring of the country's development in the past fifty years is indisputable. The Witwatersrand is to-day and has been for many years the Union's greatest railway traffic centre, and the Reef lines are now being electrified at a cost of a million pounds.

In the wider sphere the line of influence is clear. The rivalry for railway traffic to the goldfields produced economic conflict, and to the problems thus created were added those which flowed from the political and other disabilities of the mining population, leading first to the Jameson Raid and then, less than four years later, to the South African War of 1899-1902 and the annexation by Great Britain of the republics. The war prepared the way for the ultimate union of the old and new colonies, and the process was accelerated by economic forces. As a Union, South Africa has played a not unimportant part in the evolution of new relationships between Great Britain and the Dominions now defined in the Statute of Westminster as 'autonomous communities within the British Empire, equal in status and in no way subordinate one to another in any aspect of their domestic or external affairs, though united by a common allegiance to the Crown, and freely associated as members of the British Commonwealth of Nations'.

In its jubilee year, 1936, Witwatersrand gold mining is expanding on a greater scale than at any other time in its history. Only a few short years ago the decline of the industry was accepted; production seemed to have reached its peak, and falling grade, with the increased costs of deeper mining, pointed surely to a steady contraction of operations. To-day there is a new vision. A new Witwatersrand has come into view with new hope and new confidence. Built up on faith, faith in the continuity of the deposits and in the stability of gold, the Witwatersrand to-day, under the spell of the greatly increased price of its product, has unlimited faith in its own future. That faith gains strength from the example of countries which still cling tenaciously to the gold standard and of the many others which, while nominally abandoning that standard, add steadily to their holdings of the metal. An adequate substitute for gold in international relationships has yet to be devised.

The Witwatersrand mines to-day give employment to roughly 33,000 whites and 300,000 natives—over 200,000 men are daily lowered and raised by skips. The value of annual production is above £75,000,000 and profits exceed £30,000,000. In taxation and in the share of profits from lease mines, the yield to the Government is about £14,000,000, leaving £16,000,000 for dividend distribution. The balance of the revenue, about £45,000,000, goes in working costs. To-morrow, according to a recent estimate by the former Government Mining Engineer, Sir Robert Kotze, we may see an industry employing 50,000 whites and 400,000 natives, and spending in salaries, wages and stores £90,000,000, with profits and divi-

24

dends increased by at least 75 per cent. Such a forecast is necessarily based on a continuance of the price of gold now ruling and the existing level of working costs. In the view too of the present Government Mining Engineer, Dr. Hans Pirow, the future of gold mining in South Africa is secure for many decades to come. 'It is my considered opinion', he declared in a recent public address, 'that for a generation at least we can conveniently banish all talk about a waning gold mining industry. I believe that a true conception of the relatively permanent nature of this industry would lead to a better appreciation of its paramount importance in our national economy, as a South African industry worked by South Africans to the benefit of South Africa.'

In these pages we follow the growth of operations from the small beginnings in 1886 to the vast structure of to-day. The industry began on ounces to the ton; its stability to-day rests on an average recovery of less than 5 dwt. That is perhaps not quite a true comparison, for it does not take account of the great increase in the price of gold. In 1932, however, the last year under gold standard conditions, the average yield was less than $6\frac{1}{2}$ dwt. If that had been the value of ore at the surface, it would probably be true to say that the Witwatersrand conglomerates would have remained undeveloped. That $6\frac{1}{2}$ dwt. in 1932 represented 95 per cent extraction. At the stage of metallurgical science fifty years ago recovery was not more than 60 per cent, and with ore of the grade treated in 1932 the recovery would thus have been less than 5 dwt., with working costs on a far higher level than to-day. In the first actual work on the conglomerates the assays showed 5 dwt. but the reef was abandoned because of its low value. It was not until the rich Main Reef Series was discovered that the potentialities of the Witwatersrand began to be realized.

In the fifty years of development, operations have moved far away from the line of outcrop uncovered by pick and shovel, for deep level shafts are to-day sunk 10,000 feet to the south. That highly profitable operations can now be maintained at the depths to which mining has penetrated is a wonderfully impressive tribute to the great advance of engineering and metallurgical science and the high efficiency of method and administration. Indeed, in the degree of efficiency attained, the Witwatersrand gold mining industry probably stands supreme in the world.

In these pages too we may follow the rise of Johannesburg from the primitive camp of 1886 to the modern city, and the growth of settlement on the Reef generally. Johannesburg to-day is more than a mining city. It is a great industrial centre and the base of a subcontinent for trade and distribution. Nor is it preoccupied with things material. The things of the spirit also have their place, as the city's fine cathedrals, its synagogues and churches, and its great soul for charity so widely proclaim, while its advance in cultural development is marked by its flourishing university, its magnificent public library and other

Aerial view of the vast surface works of a Witwatersrand mine to-day.
Photo by Aircraft Operating Company of Africa (Pty.) Ltd., Johannesburg.

institutions. It is a city too in close touch with the world it serves, for modern invention has conquered time and distance and the days of isolation are ended. In the last few years Johannesburg and its sister communities, under the impetus of the wonderful expansion of mining, have shown a spectacular advance and builders have worked both night and day to keep pace with the great forward movement. The millions that have thus been, and are being, invested in building schemes are the best pledge that could be desired of faith and confidence in the future.

It used to be said (in Johannesburg) that there were more brains to the square inch here than in any other part of the globe, and there is no local record of that statement ever having been challenged.

The Witwatersrand goldfield stands credited in the world's ledger with a yield of 293,000,000 ounces[1] (or 10,045 tons) of gold, valued at the old standard rate at almost £1,250,000,000, or at £2,050,000,000 if estimated at the current level of sterling.

The gold in the vaults of the United States Treasury recently passed the record figure of 10,000,000,000 dollars (roughly £2,000,000,000), thus almost equalling the entire production of the world's greatest goldfield in nearly fifty years.

For their revelation both of the magnitude of Witwatersrand production and of the capacity of the United States to absorb gold, these are impressive figures.

[1] In this volume ounces represent fine ounces.

Before the Witwatersrand discoveries the Transvaal's share in world production, then scarcely more than £20,000,000, was under one per cent. It rose to a peak of 53.4 per cent in 1929 with the value of the world output at almost £83,000,000. The proportion has since fallen, partly because of the milling of a lower grade of ore and partly because of increased production in other fields, notably Russia. In 1934 (the last figures available) of a world production of 27,400,000 ounces, valued at the standard rate at £116,400,000, the Transvaal's share was 38 per cent (almost 10,500,000 ounces), in value about £45,000,000.

Transvaal production reached a peak of 11,557,858 ounces, valued at £49,094,661 (standard rate), in 1932, and then showed a steady decline as grade was lowered to meet the continuous advance in the price of gold. At the same time advantage has been taken of the opportunity greatly to expand milling and on a broader basis production is again rising. It will be assisted as new producers come into the field, whose contributions will quickly overtake any losses through exhaustion of old properties, and the prospect of the monthly production rising to the spectacular level of one million ounces (35 tons), or nearly one and a half tons a day in a working month of twenty-six days, seems very near. That figure was almost reached under the old conditions in August 1932, when the yield was 991,322 ounces.

The Witwatersrand production of 293,000,000 ounces up to the end of 1935 represents a milling of

860,000,000 tons of ore. Annual milling is now at the rate of over 40,000,000 tons. Converted to a popular illustration, that would represent sufficient rock to form seven cylindrical columns with a diameter of 100 yards each and a height of 1000 feet. There would be insuperable difficulties in raising any of these pillars, however, for the milled rock is to-day represented by the giant dumps and vast slimes dams which mark the line of the industry from one end of the reef to the other.

In main shaft sinking, main drives, cross cuts and other similar work, development footage in Witwatersrand mines has reached a total of almost 6,000 miles and is increasing at the rate of nearly 400 miles a year. The diameter of the earth at the equator is $7926\frac{1}{2}$ miles, so that the sum of Rand mining development would represent a shaft driven from one side of the earth almost to the other.

The lowest workings in one mine (the Robinson Deep) have reached the record depth of 8500 feet (2800 feet below sea level). To-day on the Rand single vertical hoists of more than 6000 feet are coming into use, travelling up to 3000 feet a minute. Though the speed for lowering and raising men is usually somewhat less than other working speeds, it seems likely that a miner will reach an underground station at a depth of 6000 feet in about three minutes, or be raised in that time. The passenger in an ordinary building lift will find it difficult to realize the significance of those figures. The working speed of the fastest lifts in South Africa is 600 feet a minute; in

New York the law at present sets a limit of 700 feet, though elevators have been installed capable of speeds up to 1200 feet. And then to visualize a vertical depth of 6000 feet. Johannesburg's tallest building, tower and mast added, will rise to a height of 260 feet, the height of St. Paul's to the top of the cross is 365 feet, of the Eiffel Tower 984 feet, and of the Empire State building, New York's tallest skyscraper, 1248 feet. Placed on top of each other these four structures would form a tower 2,857 feet high. We should have to add several other skyscrapers to present to the eye a demonstration of the meaning of a single vertical hoist of 6000 feet.

What is the ultimate practical depth of mining on the Witwatersrand? In a recent address to a scientific society the Government Mining Engineer, Dr. Pirow, said that until recently it was estimated to be 7500 feet, the main determining factors being on the one hand economic conditions and, on the other, the problems arising from temperature and humidity. Within the last few years, however, both these factors had, he said, undergone great changes. The economic factor had been altered almost out of recognition by the lower pay limit with gold at £7 an ounce, while recent research indicated that temperature and humidity could also be dealt with more adequately than was thought possible a few years ago. Hence, though very optimistic, it appeared to him to be within the range of possibility that a vertical depth of 10,000 feet might be accepted before long as the limiting depth for mining on the Rand. At a dip of approximately 25 degrees and on the assumption that only slight variations in payability and in the pay limit would take place, that increase of 2500 feet in economic workable depth would bring approximately 200,000,000 tons into the ore reserves on existing mines. Assuming an average yield of only 4 dwt. with gold at £7 an ounce, that tonnage would give a revenue of £280,000,000.

The problems arising from temperature and humidity at great depth are to-day receiving close study and attention, and experience of the greatest value will be obtained from various methods of air cooling now under trial, so that Dr. Pirow's forecast of a working depth of 10,000 feet may be within measurable distance of realization.

PART TWO

I

Origin of the Gold—Exploration and its Rewards—The Revelation of Great Riches

The staid historian will tell you that the history of the Witwatersrand gold mining industry dates from the eighties of last century when the main reefs were discovered and intensive development began, but this is a delusion. Our history really starts many millions of years before, when Nature laid the foundations of our great wealth. What we know as the Witwatersrand area was then sea coast, and a mighty river brought down from the north-west myriads of pebbles and particles of gold which it spread east and west of the present site of Johannesburg. Giving rein to our imagination, we might picture prehistoric mammoths gambolling on the beaches, and plunging about on the soft pebbly beds, thus creating the gaps and faults in the reefs encountered in present-day mining. But such a fanciful theory cannot be entertained, for there was no life existent then, as far as human knowledge goes. In later years other strata were laid down and the sea receded, and the golden beds might have been lost for eternity but for violent cataclysms which tilted them from the horizontal and left them with a dip towards the south. Thus it was that, when found a little over fifty years ago, the reefs outcropped in many places; but where they end mining and geological science have not yet determined. The question may well prove beyond human solution unless we pass to a robot era when workers will be able to penetrate to greater depths unhampered by problems of temperature and endurance.

This outline of the genesis of the Witwatersrand and the origin of its gold rests of course on mere theory, which however does provide an intelligible explanation of puzzling geological features. The gold-bearing reefs form only a very small part of a great series of sediments, 25,000 feet thick, which constitute the Witwatersrand geological system, and the order of rock succession in that series provides an unfailing guide in drilling operations to find the gold deposits where they lie at a depth far removed from any outcrop. Fortunately the gold carriers belong to the upper and not to the lower division of these sedimentary beds.

The theory also explains the presence of the water-worn pebbles which are the distinguishing feature of the Witwatersrand conglomerate reefs. How else are we to account for those pebbles, so widely distributed and persisting to unknown depths, hundreds of miles from the seaboard as we know it to-day?

The gold is contained, not in the pebbles, which you will remember were brought down separately, but in the quartzite matrix in which they are embedded. Occasionally small nuggets are found, but, unlike ordinary auriferous quartz, only rarely is gold visible in the rock. The pebbles themselves and the sheets of quartzite and shale which separate the reefs are virtually barren, and not all the pebbly reefs are payable.

The term 'banket' was early applied to the gold-bearing conglomerate beds because of their resemblance to the Dutch sweetmeat of that name containing almonds, and the world fame of the Witwatersrand has led to the adoption of the term to describe gold-bearing conglomerates in several other parts of the world.

Volumes could be written of earlier discoveries of gold in the Transvaal and in Bechuanaland, long before the opening of the Witwatersrand fields; but they were not of world importance and need not detain us.

Let us keep clear too of controversies as to who was the pioneer of all the pioneer discoverers in this area. We may recall however that as far back as 1853, more than thirty years before the launch of the industry, a prospector, Pieter Jacob Marais, exhibited in the old Volksraad (Parliament) chamber at Potchefstroom samples of gold-bearing quartz he had found on the Witwatersrand; and there are records of even earlier discoveries. But the Voortrekkers who had trekked from the Cape to escape British rule were very much averse to prospecting and had actually passed laws against it. They feared the influx of 'foreigners'. That it was not a groundless fear subsequent events were to establish, for within sixteen years of the proclamation of the Witwatersrand fields the Dutch had lost possession of their country. Under pain of death Marais became pledged not to make his discovery known to the outside world. Yet despite the official attitude to prospecting there was apparently some eagerness to learn of any payable field, for it is on record that Marais was promised a big reward for any such discovery. There is no evidence that he was successful. In later years when Republican finances were causing no little anxiety, awards for the discovery of gold in payable quantities were made.

Gold workings were established at many points before the Witwatersrand fields attracted attention, and discoveries in the Barberton district in the Eastern Transvaal caused a big influx of population in the early eighties. By the end of 1887, however, the Barberton fields were mostly deserted; they had proved impermanent. The Barberton developments nevertheless greatly facilitated the opening up of the Witwatersrand.

In their search for gold many prospectors passed over the bleak and uninviting Witwatersrand, and an Australian expert, Armfield, employed during the British occupation 1877-80 to prospect for gold, met with no success in this area which he was specially recommended to try.

Whatever the order of precedence of discoverers may be, the fact cannot be challenged that the first discovery of real importance was that by Fred Struben who, in co-operation with his brother Henry, had started prospecting on the field in 1883 and on September 18th, 1884, found a rich quartz reef, which was named Confidence, on the farm Wilgespruit, a few miles north-west of Langlaagte (where the momentous discovery of the Main Reef Series was later to be made) and about five miles north of the present town of Roodepoort. This reef proved wonderfully rich and the Strubens set up a 5-stamp battery on the property, but the reef was eventually lost. In July 1885 the Struben brothers exhibited specimens from the Confidence Reef before the Volksraad and the Executive Council in Pretoria.

As the development of the Witwatersrand was to lead to the fall of the republics, it is of ironic interest to note that the Strubens began their prospecting near the Paardekraal monument at Krugersdorp, built (to commemorate the defeat of Dingaan's Zulu hordes by the Voortrekkers) on the site where the Boers had assembled in 1880 to take oath to recover their independence and to throw off British rule.

There is abundant testimony that Fred Struben—he was the prospector and his brother financed the operations—was the first systematically to test the unique conglomerate formation of the Rand, and his was the first work done on the banket. In his prospecting of the beds, which he had traced for a great many miles, he found on the farm Honing Klip, north of Krugersdorp, in March 1885 a reef three feet in width panning 5 dwt. to the ton. He sank for ten feet on this banket. This was the pioneer work on the formation, and Struben recognized that should one of the reefs prove payable there would be work for hundreds of mills and thousands of miners.

Another early worker on the Witwatersrand or in its neighbourhood was John G. Bantjes, who formed a syndicate in Potchefstroom in 1882 to prospect the farm Kroomdraai, about six miles north-west of Krugersdorp where in 1881 an alluvial nugget of gold had been found by Fanie Minnaar of Pretoria. The farm Kromdraai was worked for gold, but the formation was quartzite and not banket. It therefore formed no part of the auriferous Witwatersrand series, nor could it properly be regarded as being in the Witwatersrand area. Bantjes and other prospectors carried their operations to the Witwatersrand late in 1884 and in 1885, and Bantjes, who first looked for the continuation of the rich Confidence Reef, turned his attention to the conglomerates on the advice of Fred Struben. He sent twenty-five tons of banket to the Strubens' mill in January 1886, the first conglomerates to be milled on the Rand, but the recovery was very disappointing. Fred Struben later struck what is now known as the Bird Reef on the farm Vogelstruisfontein, west of Langlaagte, which has proved to be of economic importance in certain areas, and Bantjes also had some important successes.

But it was the discovery of the wonderful Main Reef Series which was to transform the scene and send the call of gold to all corners of South Africa and beyond. The account here given is that which has been most widely accepted. It may, however, yet be disturbed by archive researches. The discovery was made by the merest accident. Mrs. Anna Oosthuizen, a widow living on her farm Langlaagte, three miles west of the site of Johannesburg's town hall, had engaged a roving mason, George Harrison, to build a house. Harrison was glad to undertake the task for little more than food and shelter. With a companion, George Walker, he had tramped many miles over inhospitable country and had shared many hardships. They had worked on the Barberton goldfields and were returning there from the Free State when they both found occupation: Harrison to build the house for Mrs. Oosthuizen, and Walker to work for the Strubens on their property at Wilgespruit. Harrison was still engaged on his task when he was joined by Walker, who had left the service of the Strubens. Walking through the long grass on the farm on a Sunday early in February 1886, Walker stumbled over some outcropping rock which attracted his attention. He had seen similar rock at the Strubens' mill. He broke off some pieces for panning and the pan showed a clear ring of gold. He told Harrison of his discovery, also George Honeyball, a relative of Mrs. Oosthuizen who was helping Harrison in building the house. What Walker had stumbled over proved to be the bed subsequently known as the Main Reef Leader, and it was the first actual discovery of the Main Reef Series on which the world's greatest gold mining industry has been built up. So we owe the discovery to the simple fact that the widow Oosthuizen had decided to build a house, that she had engaged the mason George Harrison to do the work, and that Harrison's friend, George Walker, had joined him at his task and had decided to take a Sunday stroll.

These then are the essential starting points in the epic of the Witwatersrand goldfields: the Strubens were the first to work the conglomerate beds, J. G. Bantjes shared in some of the earlier reef discoveries, and George Walker was the actual discoverer of the Main Reef Series.

The Strubens, who as a result of their earlier work on the conglomerates had secured options on many farms, and Bantjes, who formed one of the earliest gold mining companies, reaped the reward of their enterprises, but Walker was unable to turn his success to much personal advantage. He failed in a quest for funds to carry on further prospecting, returned to find the discovery widely known, and, unable to provide the money, had to give up the year's prospecting rights he had secured for £60. He was however given two claims[1] on the site of his discovery, one of which he subsequently sold for £350; the other he gave to his mate Harrison who seems soon to have disappeared from the scene.

Walker died a poor man at the age of seventy-one on September 18th, 1924, his last days relieved from care by a grant from the Chamber of Mines made when he was 'rediscovered' a few years before his death. Honeyball has lived to see the jubilee of the fields.

[1] A claim is 150 feet broad and 400 feet long, the breadth measured along the strike of the reef and the length in the direction of the dip.

II

How the Vision Grew—Kimberley Sees the Gold—The Rush to the Rand—Rhodes and Robinson: a Contrast

A great deal of further prospecting had to be done before the significance of the strike was demonstrated. But with the new information at their disposal Fred Struben and Bantjes were soon at work on different portions of the farm Vogelstruisfontein, west of Langlaagte. Both succeeded in locating the Main Reef Series and it was on Vogelstruisfontein that Struben subsequently sank the first shaft on the reefs to a depth of about forty feet. Trial crushings of twenty-five tons of Main Reef Leader at the Strubens' mill yielded twenty-six ounces of gold over the plates.

Other gold seekers came on the scene, and within a short time the Main Reef had been located from the farm Luipaardsvlei (Krugersdorp) on the west to Driefontein (Boksburg) on the east, a distance of about thirty miles, by outcrops and cuttings through surface soil. Though the reef outcropped over considerable distances, great lengths were hidden by a few feet of surface soil. Because the formation was new to them, most prospectors were unable to discriminate one rock from another and had to rely on panning and assaying, since the Main Reef and its associates were similar to other reefs which were not consistent gold carriers. The method of prospecting adopted was to cut through the surface soil across the strike, thus uncovering the various beds occurring in the series. Beds which gave signs of being of a conglomerate structure were submitted to panning and assaying and, if found to be gold-bearing, were uncovered along the strike so as to obtain length of reef to determine the value. Should this be promising a winze was put down on the dip of the bed and its value tested in depth.

When these developments were in progress, news of the discoveries and of the exceptional values that were being obtained spread slowly through the country, for means of communication were primitive in those days and reports could not readily be confirmed. But when men began to whisper to each other wonderful stories that were coming through from the Witwatersrand the gold fever rapidly developed. It infected rich and poor alike. Pannings of ore brought from the new fields excited their interest and made them restless. Early in July 1886, on a visit to Potchefstroom to raise £2000 for the purchase of a small battery, Bantjes met Fred W. Alexander, a Kimberley merchant on his way to Barberton in search of gold. Bantjes showed him samples of the banket and panned them. So impressed was Alexander that he abandoned his Barberton enterprise, travelled by wagon to the Rand, inspected Bantjes's proposition and agreed to provide the money for one-eighth interest in the syndicate. He sped back to Kimberley with samples and invited prominent Kimberley men to see the panning. This demonstration took place on July 16th. Cecil Rhodes, J. B. Robinson (afterwards Sir Joseph) and many other men who were later to play a big part in opening up the Rand were present. The panning showed a wonderful prospect and Alexander could have raised much more than the £2000 he required.

Thus were the riches of the Rand brought to Kimberley and in this way too the interest of other centres in South Africa was excited.

A wonderful impetus was at once given to the movement already in progress both from the Cape and Natal to the new land of promise. The nearest railheads in those days, as has been stated, were Kimberley and Ladysmith—Kimberley about 300 miles by road and Ladysmith a little less—so transport was a difficult problem. The existing coach services were speedily overwhelmed, though they were supplemented, particularly from Kimberley, varying rates being quoted for special coaches, fast coaches, ordinary coaches and slow coaches. These developments are distant only fifty years, but fifty years of amazing advance in travel. No air services then, of course, for that was twenty-three years before Bleriot crossed the English Channel and he was then but a mere boy of fourteen. It was decades earlier than the motor car and motor cycle, and the common bicycle had not yet reached the pneumatic tyre stage of its development.

45

In almost every town and village in South Africa the talk was of gold, as it had been fifteen years earlier of diamonds, and everywhere syndicates were being formed to make a bid for fortune in the north. Vehicles of all descriptions were pressed into service, from the light buggy to the heavy wagon, and it is not difficult therefore to picture the excitement of the preparations for the long trek and the scenes on the dusty and windswept tracks from the Cape and Natal in this 'race' for the Witwatersrand, enterprises attended by no little anxiety for individual parties lest they should arrive to find no claims left for them. Along the established highways and the veld roads they came with such camp equipment as they were able to transport, with wheelbarrows, picks and shovels, and the indispensable pestle, mortar and pan. For some it was a journey of days, for others weeks, but for all the same goal and the same hope. The fact that a man had no money in his pockets did not deter him from the enterprise; if he felt the call, as many such did, he tramped it.

As many as forty spans of mules were used on the 300-mile coach journey from Kimberley to the Rand and the changing at the frequent stages was done in remarkably quick time. The ordinary fare for the journey, which when all went well took about five days, was £12 10s. for an inside seat and £10 outside.

In one of the first coaches leaving Kimberley for the north after the panning demonstration by Fred W. Alexander was J. B. Robinson, with a telegram in his pocket from an agent in Pretoria (Charles Evans) reading: 'A discovery made about thirty miles from Pretoria of conglomerate shedding gold. Think it worth your while to come up and see it.' Evans had once worked a diamond claim in Kimberley for Robinson on a fifty-fifty basis. In the same coach were Dr. Hans Sauer (to act for Cecil Rhodes) and Alexander.

Direct service with the Rand had not then been established, and at Potchefstroom passengers for the Rand had to make their own arrangements for transport for the 80 mile journey. Robinson engaged a wagon and mules and gave Sauer a seat. After a close inspection of cuttings where the banket has been exposed and after making many pannings which showed excellent results, Robinson came to bold decisions. He saw that the outcrop extended for thirty miles or more and on this based a conviction that there must be good depth to it. He purchased the Langlaagte property from the widow Oosthuizen (now in her new house) for £6000, after a preliminary lease, and in a few weeks had acquired properties at a total cost of £26,000. Within a few years those properties were capitalized at £4,000,000, while the share value at one time rose to £18,000,000. Still in the early days of the field, Robinson was fired with the ambition to launch a mining property which would eclipse in magnitude all his previous undertakings. It was this ambition which led to the formation of Randfontein Estates with a nominal capital of £2,000,000. As the Main Reef had been pegged off east and west to its proved extent, the continuation then being lost, Robinson decided on a systematic investigation of the Western Rand and his prospectors picked up the reef on the farm Randfontein and followed it over other farms. The area embraced in the company subsequently formed was 40,000 acres and the distance along the outcrop of the formation was nearly ten miles.

Robinson kept the control of all his companies practically in his own hands until, in less prosperous days, in December 1916, his interests were taken over by the Johannesburg Consolidated Investment Company.

Against Robinson's confidence, Rhodes's hesitation stands in sharp contrast. On his first visit, when he travelled with Robinson, Dr. Sauer secured representative samples of the banket and hastened back to Kimberley. Two mornings after his return he was on the way again to the Rand with Rhodes and C. D. Rudd, so closely associated with Rhodes in his enterprises. The coach for the first time in the history of the service was diverted from Potchefstroom to cross the Rand on its way to Pretoria.

Working on Rhodes's behalf, Sauer secured options on properties from which in later years millions of gold were produced. The negotiations were complete; all that remained was the signing of Rhodes's name. But before his signature had been secured he left hurriedly for Kimberley on receipt of news that his friend Neville Pickering could not live much longer. With Pickering he stayed to the end and Sauer could get no answer to repeated urgent messages. In this way options which would have given Rhodes a dominating position in the new goldfields had perforce to be abandoned. When Rhodes returned to the Rand he was still in time to secure some valuable properties, the negotiations again being conducted by Sauer.

But there is nothing to show that Rhodes was ever enthusiastic over the prospects of the goldfields. The advice of his own expert, Gardner Williams (afterwards general manager of De Beers), was against extensive commitments, as in Williams's view the banket was only a 10 dwt. proposition, which in those days of high costs and poor recovery was a vastly different story from ounces-to-the-ton reefs. How elated company managements would be to work 10 dwt. reefs to-day! Rhodes did, however, put forward to other large holders a scheme for an amalgamation of interests and some tentative agreement was reached; afterwards some differences arose and the scheme was abandoned. The formation of the Consolidated Gold Fields of South Africa in 1887 arose out of this early idea of amalgamation, the company acquiring all the interests of Rhodes and his syndicates.

Apart from his technical advice there were doubtless other good reasons which made Rhodes cautious. Perhaps there was a reluctance to place capital in territory where it might not easily be controlled and where there might be unsympathetic treatment. The big battle for control at Kimberley had yet to be faced and there were the ambitious schemes of northern expansion to be carried through.

It was Rhodes's luck that the world wanted diamonds and was able to pay for them at the time that he wanted millions to finance his great enterprises; a diamond depression such as South Africa has known in the last few years would have gravely affected his projects. It is conceivable even that the course of South African history might have been changed, for there might have been no Chartered Company and no Mashonaland occupation.

III

Launch of the Industry—Riches for the Poor — Pioneer Companies — The First Mining

The Witwatersrand gold mining industry was formally launched by the announcement which appeared in the Government Gazette (Staats Courant) of the South African Republic of September 8th, 1886, fixing the dates for the proclamation as public diggings of farms along the line of outcrop from Boksburg to Krugersdorp. The historic date of the first proclamation was September 20th; others were to follow at intervals of a week, the last on October 11th. The list included the Government ground of Randjeslaagte which was afterwards set apart for the township; and this has created some confusion about the date of the birth of Johannesburg itself. Of the township, as will be seen, there was no formal proclamation, and Johannesburg's history may fairly be said to have begun with the first sale of building sites on December 8th, 1886.

The issue of claim licences was in the hands of the farmers themselves until the Government appointed Jan Meyer, the district veld cornet (resident Government representative), as gold commissioner; and he had as his assistant Paxton de Roi. Meyer had played no small part in locating outcrops of the Main Reef Series. As veld cornet one of his duties was to accompany the Inspection Commission delimiting the boundaries of unsurveyed farms and reporting on all Government ground intervening. This gave him an excellent opportunity to observe where banket outcropped, and many of the early reef discoveries were due to his vigilance. Meyer subsequently became associated with a friend, Charlton, in the opening of the Meyer and Charlton mine which developed into one of the most prosperous Rand producers, being closed down only in 1932 when its ground had been exhausted.

The revenue from claim licences was at first drawn in full by the owners of the farms, but when farms were proclaimed half the licence money went to the Government. The Government issue of licences began in July 1886 from two tents pitched on the veld near the present township of Jeppestown. A small two-roomed stone building erected there later has been authoritatively stated to have been the first building on the Rand.

It was on Meyer's report as gold commissioner that the reefs were rich enough to warrant the proclamation of the ground, that the Government appointed Johan Rissik and Christian Johannes Joubert as a commission of inquiry. Their report being favourable, the Government decided on the first proclamations and appointed a mining commissioner, Captain von Brandis. From his tent pitched on the site in lower Market Street where the coach-building works of Wevell Bros. were later established, he read the first proclamations on September 20th, 1886.

If farmers in the Heidelberg district south of Johannesburg had had their way, the goldfields would not have been proclaimed. In a memorial to the President they 'strongly objected to be surrounded by so much bustle and excitement in the form of a large working population' and pleaded instead for a policy of concessions to farmers to work their own farms for gold should the metal be found thereon in payable quantities. But the objections of the Heidelberg farmers, in their own interests as events were to prove, were wisely disregarded.

Before the proclamation of the farms as public diggings big sums of money had changed hands. Sudden wealth had come to men who had never before known riches, pastoralists who had had a hard struggle for existence with small herds of cattle and sheep. Agriculturally the land was of little value, and many stories have been told of farms sold for such more highly prized assets as a wagon and span of oxen. The gold discoveries changed all that, and from a condition of poverty these pastoralists, or a great many of them, suddenly found themselves overwhelmed with money. Where farms were not sold outright at high figures (over £10,000 in many cases), a heavy price was received for prospecting contracts, with the option to purchase, and big revenues were drawn from claim licences.

The simple folk who sold their farms to strangers or granted prospecting rights were taking no risks. Sovereigns were real tangible things which could be counted one by one, stacked in neat piles, and then safely hidden away in the house. Bank deposits and interest payments these people did not understand; cheques and banknotes they did not trust. Some engaging stories of the transactions of those and later days have been recalled. An old Voortrekker who had sold his farm for a large sum had stipulated that the money should be paid in gold coin on his table. When the time for payment approached he was coaxed into a bank manager's office and told through an interpreter that if he would accept payment there the bank would, if he wished, look after his money for him and pay him interest on it. His suspicions thoroughly aroused, the old man broke off the negotiations. He could understand the bank keeping the money in its safe and charging him for looking after it, but there must surely be a catch in a suggestion to keep his money and also pay him interest. He insisted on the cash being taken to his farm and counted out on his table. In the parcelling out of the proceeds of a prospecting contract, £2000, there were nine owners and no two held equal shares. The division proved an insuperable mathematical task for them and the farm schoolmaster was called in. After many efforts he announced that whichever way he calculated it there was £100 over. In the circumstances he was allowed to keep that, and who can say he did not earn it? A farmer who had never handled more than about £12 a year was suddenly in the position of drawing £500 a month from claim licences. The worry of looking after so much money was too much for him, he confessed. He became ill and died within three months.

Perhaps the most fortunate of the farm holders on the Witwatersrand in those early days were those who received large sums in option money and still retained possession of their farms because payable reefs were not discovered. They were not therefore under the necessity of seeking new homes. It was good business for them, but poor business for unfortunate pioneering syndicates which in this way lost much money which they could never recover.

Witwatersrand gold production began in May 1887, and in view of the fact that the deposits were at the surface and that there were no mining problems such as we know to-day, it may seem surprising that an earlier start was not made. But it must not be forgotten that every bit of machinery had to be brought hundreds of miles by slow road transport from distant railheads. Road conditions fifty years ago may safely be left to the imagination. Broken-down vehicles and stranded machinery told an eloquent tale of these transport difficulties, and it was a matter for surprise how different sections of plant, separated to fit the accommodation available, were ever reassembled and restored as working units.

The pioneer producing company was the Wemmer.

which provided a picturesque illustration of the romance of early mining enterprise. The company's claims adjoined those of the Ferreira where the reef outcropped. A deep cutting was made to locate the outcrop in the Wemmer ground without success and the baffled workers were considering what next to do, when a Dutch lad who had watched the operations for several days offered for a reward of five pounds to point out the reef. His offer promptly accepted, the lad led the way to a small piece of isolated embedded rock. It was indeed the outcrop, for the test showed nine ounces to the ton, and the youth was cheerfully paid his reward. So successful was the Wemmer that within a month on the initial capital of £5000 a dividend of 40 per cent was paid. After a remarkably profitable record the company was merged in March 1905 in the Village Main Reef. In its short life it had paid £871,180 in dividends.

The Wemmer, as stated, was the first producer. Actually the pioneer flotation was the Witwatersrand Gold Mining Company (East Rand) which was brought out in Kimberley on September 4th, 1886, with a capital of £210,000. Its promotor was a Kimberley financier, William Knight, who showed such confidence in the venture that when the public subscribed only £11,000 out of £30,000 required for working capital he closed the lists and took up the balance of the shares himself. He never had reason to regret his confidence. After many changes in its capital and claim holdings the company still survives among Witwatersrand producers.

The edifice of the world's greatest gold mining industry has been built up from crude beginnings. In the earliest operations the general method of mining adopted was that of open cuttings or trenches dug along the outcrops of the reef, some of which were put down to depths of 60 feet or more. At first the ore, which was easy to mine, was thrown up by natives from bench to bench, but, as the cuttings became deeper, other means had to be adopted. In some cases whims and whips worked by oxen and mules were employed, in others the ore was raised by windlasses worked by hand labour.

The pioneer 'crushing plant' in the Transvaal, at Eersteling, near Pietersburg, was a huge dolerite boulder weighing about 1100 lb. rocked backward and forward on a hard schist bed. Under the boulder the ore was crushed and the gold concentrated. The boulder may be seen in the Pretoria Museum. At some points on the Witwatersrand the earliest form of battery was a 'dolley' consisting of two uprights with a crossbar over which a long pole was balanced, with a heavy weight at one end. It was worked by a native who let the weight drop on to the ore held in a box through which water flowed, depositing the gold on blankets spread out in front. Two, three and five stamp mills were erected where there was water, instead of water being pumped to the mills. The value set on such water sites is well illustrated by the inaugural speech of the chairman of one company who congratulated shareholders on having the battery on a spruit (little stream) 'because the water would carry away the tailings and avoid accumulation'. And yet those tailings took away about 40 per cent of the gold; under the methods then in operation recovery was not more than about 60 per cent. When the ore had been crushed by the stamps the pulp flowed over amalgamation tables which held the freed gold, or at least so much of it as did not run away in tailings. The prospectus of one of the pioneering companies stated: 'The water is nine or ten miles distant from the claims but the road towards the water is almost wholly sloping.' Companies were glad to sell tailings to builders and plasterers at five shillings a Scotch cartload, so it is true to say that many of the early houses in Johannesburg were literally plastered with gold.

Ore was conveyed in wagons or Scotch carts to the pioneer mills on these water sites. The Wemmer had its 3-stamp battery at the side of a stream about four miles to the south of its claims. The Ferreira, another of the earliest companies, had a 5-stamp battery at Auckland Park, also about four miles away, and the carts transporting the ore crossed the ground on which the city is now built. The Jubilee company's first crushing equipment was on the Natal Spruit, a mile or two away, and so rich was the ore that the carts transporting it were lined with sacking to prevent any loss of gold.

The first 2000 tons of ore from the Crown Reef, one of the outcrop companies of the large amalgamation known to-day as the Crown Mines, were crushed at the Strubens' mill, nine miles away.

For steam-driven plants the cost of fuel was a serious handicap. At first the only supply was bush timber, but coal became available in 1887.

Under all these conditions it will be realized that at the opening of the fields working costs were very high and thus only the rich ore could be worked. Fortunately that was ore yielding ounces to the ton.

IV

Early Judgments—Tragedies of the House of Barnato — The First Boreholes — The Sceptics Confounded—Cyanide Saves the Industry

In these days, when the reefs have been followed to vertical depths of 7000 and 8000 feet, it seems strangely unreal to recall that the first problem that divided the mining experts was whether the deposit was merely superficial or whether it persisted to any depth. The sceptics were baffled by the unique character of the formation; and the developments confounded them.

Some of the very early judgments on the fields make entertaining reading. 'Altogether there is reason to believe', wrote an observer of July 1886, 'that the deposit on the average is not more than from ten feet to fifteen feet in depth, and, rich though it is, machinery of some sort is required for the extraction of the gold. If the line of deposit can be traced, as stated, for fifty or sixty miles, it will be strange if some place cannot be found where payable gold may be obtained by the ordinary sluicing process.' A correspondent of the *Transvaal Advertiser*, published in Pretoria, wrote in August 1886: 'In some places the deposit is much deeper than was at first supposed, a shaft having been sunk to a depth of fifty-four feet without reaching bottom. The samples which are brought in continue to be rich in character, but until something more definite has been done than crushing specimens it would be premature to express any opinion as to the intrinsic value of the field as a gold-bearing area.' The correspondent of a Kimberley newspaper was 'amazed at the prices being paid for claims, as much as fifty pounds' and asked: 'What can these reckless speculators do with their property without water and machinery? None of the reefs has been sufficiently proved in bulk to justify what cannot but be an unwise acquisition of property which may or may not be worth the money paid for it. If people were to turn their attention to the discovery of other than banket reefs which must exist in the neighbourhood of the Rand, it would pay them much better, but everybody seems to leave that to chance.'

And wisely too, so it seems.

Rhodes's expert, as we have seen, advised him against making any plunge. Barney Barnato, the man who was to fight with Rhodes a losing battle for the control of Kimberley's diamonds, and who ultimately played a big part in the development of the Rand, brought two mining experts to the fields in 1887 and their reports induced him, at that time, to leave the Rand severely alone. In their view, and that of many others, the outcrops of reef were merely the elevated beds of old watercourses and the auriferous rock, therefore, would not extend to any depth. In the following year, however, Barnato became convinced that the Rand was to become a bigger thing than Kimberley, and he set to work, with a rapidity that amazed his competitors, to acquire not merely mining propositions but also real estate. Of both, within two months, he became the largest holder.

Barnato's end was tragic. The slump caused by the Jameson Raid, which took him completely by surprise, involved him in heavy losses and his health broke down. He was drowned at sea near Madeira when on a recuperative voyage to England in June 1897 in the steamer *Scot*. His body was recovered. The ship's fourth officer, W. T. Clifford, who had with great pluck plunged into the sea to his rescue was picked up in a state of exhaustion.

'It's awful work being a millionaire,' Barnato had once remarked to a friend. 'You can envy me if you like, but you don't know what it is to be hunted about from morning till night, never to have a moment to yourself, to feel that you must go on, you can't stop, other people won't let you stop—it's weary work, weary work.'

Less than a year later, on March 14th, 1898, another tragedy befell the house of Barnato, Woolf Joel, nephew of Barnato, being shot dead in his office in Johannesburg by a German blackmailer, Franz Ludwig Kurt von Veltheim. Acquitted on a charge of murder on a plea of self-defence, von Veltheim was deported. Found by the British authorities as a prisoner of war in Pretoria in 1900, he was again sent out of the country and in 1908 was sentenced in London to twenty years' penal servitude for demanding, with menaces, £16,000 from S. B. Joel, Woolf Joel's brother. His sentence was reduced in 1910 by five years, and during the Great War, when released from jail, he was interned. Repatriated to Germany in 1919, he received another sentence of imprisonment in 1924 for obtaining money by false pretences. In later years he reappeared twice in South Africa, professedly on expeditions to find hidden gold, and on each occasion was promptly deported as an undesirable, the ban imposed in 1898 never having been raised. Von Veltheim died a few years ago and with him died whatever secret of hidden treasure there may have been.

When the first mining companies were formed there was little demand for claims which did not include the outcrop, for no one knew whether the reefs would persist in depth or whether they would peter out, as the pessimists foretold, at fifty or sixty feet; time and development alone would decide. Very early in the operations, however, the reefs were found to dip to the south, and ideas regarding the value of ground adjoining the outcrop claims at once began to change. Thus a second line of companies, a little farther south, came into being in 1888 and 1889. They were named deep-level companies because vertical shafts had to be sunk to cut the reefs, but they were not deep-level companies as the description is understood to-day, for the reef horizons were not more than 300 or 400 feet from the surface.

As the reefs were followed in depth they showed a flattening tendency and then the true significance of the dip began to dawn. On the theory that, at the angle of dip, the Main Reef Series would pass out of the vertical boundaries of a single or a double row of claims at no great depth, a borehole was commenced in December 1889 on the Village Main Reef, on the southern border of Johannesburg. The borehole reached a depth of 665 feet in March 1890 and within three months the existence of a greater Rand had been established. The drill cut the South Reef at 517 feet. It measured two feet in width and six inches of it assayed 9 oz. 12 dwt. to the ton. The Main Reef Leader was struck at 581 feet and assayed 11 dwt.

Here was sensational confirmation of the correctness of the calculations on which the drilling was based; the continuation of the banket reefs in depth and value had been clearly demonstrated.

The Village Main Reef's was the first borehole put down on the Rand. It was only a few hundred feet from the line of outcrop and the reefs were cut at depths which, under prospecting conditions to-day, were certainly comparatively shallow, but it was an enterprise which heralded a wonderful expansion of activity.

The lead of the Village Main Reef was followed by many other companies whose boreholes proved the continuity of the reefs at far greater but still workable depths, thousands of feet away from the outcrop.

At a very early stage of its existence the gold mining industry was saved by cyanide.

Amalgamation was the only method used for the recovery of gold up to 1890, the average recovery being then about 64 per cent. Later by concentration methods the overall recovery was brought up to about 74 per cent. As the mines became deeper, however, the ore became pyritic and thus more refractory and the recovery fell to less than 60 per cent, a development which gave a shock to confidence, for a loss of 40 per cent meant thirty-four shillings in every ounce of fine gold at eighty-five shillings.

At this anxious stage, towards the end of 1890, the McArthur-Forrest cyanide process was introduced and it proved the salvation of the industry, for not only the oxidized ore but the pyritic ore as well was found to be amenable to the treatment. In the process the ore is dissolved in a cyanide solution from which it is precipitated by contact with zinc. Cyaniding was not without its difficulties, but these were gradually overcome and the process was established in general use.

The product of crushing is in two forms, sands and slime. At first the cyanide process could be made to deal only with the leachable product, the sands, and the millmen were concerned to prevent the formation of the unleachable slime. But the problem of treating the slime received constant attention and another milestone in the progress of Rand metallurgy was reached in 1894 when a decantation process for slimes was introduced, leading in 1896 to the start of

E   65

the first decantation plant. It was immediately successful and thus for the first time in the history of the fields the complete treatment of the whole of the ore became possible. Many advances in the cyanide process have since been made and the solutions to-day are only a fraction of the strength formerly used. As a result of these improvements, coupled with revolutionary changes in methods of ore crushing, the overall recovery from all sources to-day varies from 92 to 98 per cent. Treatment plants are not of equal efficiency and other important factors are the varying nature of the ore, and the degree of grinding necessary. If we take the average recovery at 95 per cent, with gold say at one hundred and forty shillings an ounce, the value of unrecovered gold is seven shillings of every ounce. As the average monthly production is well over 900,000 ounces, it will be seen that the opportunities for metallurgical science are not yet closed. The flotation process may provide the line for further advance; it is under trial and investigation.

V

Railways Come after Difficulties—Demonstration against President Kruger—The Drifts Crisis—Share Speculation—Jameson Raid and the War—Standard of Production

The Boer leaders in the Transvaal were shrewd enough to realize that railways were inevitable and, in fact, as early as 1884 had granted a concession to Hollander and German capitalists, a grant which led to the formation of the Netherlands S.A. Railway Company. Backveld sentiment however was strongly against railways if only for the reason that they would ruin transport riding, which brought great profit. It was in submission to such prejudice that the first railway along the Witwatersrand, primarily a coal line, was named the 'Rand Tram'. In prospecting for gold, coal had been discovered in the Boksburg district in December 1887 and hundreds of wagons were soon conveying the sorely needed fuel to mines along the Reef. The pioneer railway, opened on March 17th, 1890, linked Johannesburg with Boksburg; in 1891 it was extended to Springs on the east and Krugersdorp on the west, and in this year also Pretoria was linked by rail with the Rand.

The urgency of the need for railway communication with the coast had been vividly impressed on the authorities by the peril of starvation which the mining community faced in the later months of 1889. In a prolonged drought Transvaal crops had failed and the supplies of food on hand (and coming forward) for 25,000 whites and 15,000 natives would soon have been exhausted. This was one of the first problems which faced the newly constituted Chamber of Mines. Acting on petitions which flowed in, the Government suspended special duties on certain foodstuffs and made a relief grant of £5000. This the Chamber of Mines allocated to a bonus scheme of twenty pounds each to the first 250 wagoners to reach Johannesburg from beyond the border with flour, Boer meal, mealies or mealie meal. The Natal Government offered an equal bonus to the first fifty wagoners reaching Johannesburg from Charlestown, the Natal border town. Both ox and mule teams were engaged in this transport 'Derby', which achieved its object, and nearly 300 claims were admitted for full or partial bonus.

While the great necessity for railway links with the coast was realized, republican policy sought to delay connection with the Cape and Natal until the Delagoa Bay line had been built, for no part of that line would be under British control and for most of its distance it would be in Transvaal territory.

It was this official attitude that led to a demonstration against President Kruger on a visit to Johannesburg in March 1890, when the demand for railways was again pressed. Speaking to a crowd of 5000 at the Wanderers, who had dissembled their love for him with such loyal outbursts as 'God Save the Queen' and 'Rule, Britannia', he said he was glad to see the diggers. He knew they had come to make money and then leave the country. They were welcome to take all the gold they could, but, as for railways, he would allow no line to be built until the railway from Delagoa Bay had been completed. After the meeting, held in the afternoon, the republican flag was torn from the flagstaff in front of the public buildings on the Market Square and in the evening there was a demonstration, which called for the intervention of the police, outside the house of the chief magistrate, Captain von Brandis, where the President spent the night.

Portuguese progress with railway construction proved to be slow and the connection with Delagoa Bay was not made until October 20th, 1894, more than two years after the Cape-Rand line had been completed. This was opened on September 15th, 1892. The Natal line was opened on December 15th, 1895.

In September 1895 the Transvaal Government, in its effort to encourage trade through Delagoa Bay, had imposed prohibitive rates on the thirty miles of railway from the Cape within the Transvaal border, and this led to the drifts crisis. The Cape's reply was to unload goods at certain drifts over the Vaal River and to send them on to Johannesburg by wagon. President Kruger met this move by closing the drifts, a violation of the London Convention which governed the relations between Britain and the Republic. The British Government, to which the Cape Government appealed, took up a strong attitude and there was a danger of war; but the Transvaal gave way and the drifts were reopened in November.

The division of the traffic spoils between the three competitive railway systems was for a great many years a leading problem in South African affairs. The difficulty did not disappear with Union, for it survives in the conflict of interest with Mozambique, whose bargaining counter has been the supply of native labour to the mines.

The second railway connection with the Cape, via Fourteen Streams, was made only a few years before Union, in April 1906.

The mining industry at its birth was almost overwhelmed in a flood of company promotion, with over-capitalization and over-speculation. From about seventy companies with a nominal capital of over £3,000,000 in 1887, the number rose in a little over two years to 450 with a nominal capital of about £11,000,000. On the stock exchange list there were no fewer than 300 companies. A great many disappeared in the first market collapse but even in 1893 gold mining companies in existence in the Transvaal numbered 183. Of these 104 were 'off gold' and 'off gold' most of them remained, never emerging from the nebulous stage 'development and equipment'. History has unhappily repeated itself in later years, as so many unfortunate shareholders can testify by reference to their share portfolios.

The first share dealings took place in June 1887 on a site somewhere near the Ferreira and Wemmer claims, the business being conducted from a tent. Livery stables opposite the present Central Hotel at the corner of Commissioner Street and Sauer Street provided the next site, and later on an exchange was set up at the intersection of Commissioner Street and Simmonds Street, opposite Corner House. With the growth of business better facilities were provided for the public to lose money and the exchange was housed in the building now known as the Palladium Theatre. From here it was removed in 1904 to the present buildings in Hollard Street, nearer the police headquarters known as Marshall Square. The police raised no objections.

Code books in the early days of share dealing on the Rand were not so elaborate as they are to-day and mistakes were sometimes made, but they were not always costly. In one instance which may be quoted a cable was read as an instruction to buy 5000 City and Suburbans at a limit of five shillings over the market price. The shares were easily secured, but in checking the cable a few days later the discovery was made that it had nothing to do with City and Suburbans. Meantime however these shares had risen to a high price and a big profit was made.

In the undisciplined days when the home of the Stock Exchange was in Simmonds Street, brokers came out into the open to deal, and this business became so active that the roadway between Commissioner Street and Market Street was closed by posts and chains to vehicular traffic. With the general devotion to share dealing, 'between the chains' became an intimate part of Johannesburg's life. Even on Sundays the business continued and became such a scandal that the police stepped in and stopped it.

In the first days of share dealing Kimberley and Natal interests were in control, having provided most of the money for opening up the properties; but with the broadening of outlook London became a big factor and Paris later joined in. When the first fever of speculation was at its height, in the early part of 1889, big operators had to devise bold competitive measures. Telegraphic delays were frequently serious, messages being often held up for a week or ten days, and at times there were big margins between Johannesburg and London prices or even between those of Johannesburg and other South African centres. The Transvaal Government elected to give preference to messages within its own borders; other messages could take their chance. It was this practice that big operators turned to advantage by establishing their own dispatch service between Malmani, near the western border of the Transvaal, and Mafeking, just over the border. Telegrams sent to Malmani, being a station within the republic, suffered no delay and from Malmani mounted runners took them to Mafeking where the telegraph was again used. With inward messages the process was reversed. Many were the horses used up in this way, but gamblers were bidding for high stakes.

In the collapse which followed the 1888-9 boom, brokers vainly endeavoured to revive interest by auction sales of shares 'between the chains'. Blocks of thousands of shares were sold for a few pounds. That was full value in many instances, but there were exceptions. Thus a parcel of Klipriversberg Estates (now City Deep) was sold at one shilling and sixpence a share. When confidence was once again restored Klipriversbergs rose to £17 10s.

There were some who took a very gloomy view of the first setback. 'Johannesburg is very different, indeed, from the Johannesburg it was but can never be again,' wrote one sad commentator, 'a fitting tribute to the rascality that has brought an undoubtedly good goldfield to ruin, financial and social.' How well we have built on those ruins!

Perhaps one of Johannesburg's best efforts in share speculation was the gamble in Coronation Syndicates in 1911. That was the year of the coronation of King George V, and this event was the inspiration for the name of the syndicate. Of more immediate importance however was the inspiration for market dealings in the shares, and this came from the circulation of most glowing reports regarding the gold value of the farms, south-east of the Rand, from Heidelberg to Greylingstad, over which the syndicate held options. The £100 shares rose to no less than £2800 and then became almost unsaleable when an expert's examination failed to justify the reports.

The fortunes of Johannesburg and the Witwatersrand generally are so closely allied to the gold mining industry that the share market will continue to be the barometer of the prevailing mood, whether of optimism or depression. Gold however has not always held the stage to the exclusion of other interests, for diamond, platinum and other booms have added variety to the chronicle, and, given further opportunities, may do so again.

It is not proposed in this little volume to trace at length the political developments which led to the Jameson Raid at the end of 1895 and to the South African War of 1899-1902; the record of those events can be studied in the fullest detail in the many publications devoted to them. They form however so essential a part of the story of the Rand that they cannot be excluded from any chronicle, however brief.

It was the failure of the 'uitlander' (alien) population, as the British and other newcomers were regarded, to obtain redress of political grievances that gave birth to the Raid conspiracy with which Rhodes, then Prime Minister of the Cape Colony, was so closely associated. The scheme was simplicity itself. Forces were to be secretly armed, the arsenal at Pretoria was to be seized, the 'uitlanders' in Johannesburg were to rise and hold the town, and Jameson was to dash in to their assistance with a force of 800 men. And then?—well, it was the eleventh hour confusion regarding the final objective that, with other causes, was responsible for the delay in the execution of the plot. The reform leaders in Johannesburg did not seek the overthrow of the republic and it was because of mistrust on this point that they decided to postpone action. But Jameson could not brook delay and on December 29th, 1895, crossed the Transvaal border from Bechuanaland with a much smaller force than had been contemplated.

The conspiracy never had a hope of success. Johannesburg, hampered by the difficulties in smuggling in arms for distribution, was ill equipped for action, the scheme for seizing the arsenal at Pretoria became impracticable because at the time the town was thronged with Boers, and any attempt at a rising was foredoomed to failure. Such arms as were available were given out, and, under the control of the Reform Committee which had been hurriedly constituted, order was maintained. It was a time of feverish excitement and great anxiety, if not of panic, with the wildest rumours in circulation. Business had come to a standstill and all mining work virtually ceased. The trains to Natal and the Cape were crowded with refugees, mostly women and children, and in the turmoil produced by the Raid came the shock of a railway disaster, one of the refugee trains being wrecked near Glencoe on the Natal line on December 31st, with the loss of 36 lives.

The defeat and surrender of Jameson's force at Doornkop, south-west of Roodepoort, on January 2nd, 1896, brought the wreck of the whole conspiracy, and with failure came the penalty of exposure and retribution—the imprisonment of Jameson and his principal officers, the downfall of Rhodes, and the arrest and punishment of the members of the Reform Committee on a charge of high treason. Of the four leaders, Lionel Phillips, Col. Frank Rhodes [1] (brother of Cecil Rhodes), John Hays Hammond, and George Farrar[2], who were sentenced to death at the trial in April 1896, and whose sentences were commuted to fines of £25,000 each, two, Sir Lionel Phillips and J. H. Hammond, still happily live[3] in enjoyment of their reprieve. They will have a close interest in the jubilee year celebrations, for it was by the faith and vision of such men as Phillips in the very earliest days of the fields that the foundations of the great industry were laid, and by the skill of such men as Hammond that rapid advance was made in the solution of its engineering problems.

The short years which followed the Raid with its legacy of suspicion and mistrust did not bring any amelioration of the condition of the uitlanders, rather the reverse, which perhaps was not altogether surprising, and early in 1899 came the initiation of the second reform movement whose outcome was the petition to Queen Victoria signed by 21,000 British subjects, stating the uitlander position. Then followed the despatches and negotiations leading to the presentation on October 9th of the Boer ultimatum to the British Government. Two days later Britain

[1] Died May 19th, 1915.
[2] Died September 21st, 1905
[3] Just as these pages are going to press, the death is announced, first, of John Hays Hammond, and then of Sir Lionel Phillips.

and the republics (for the Free State had thrown in its lot with the Transvaal) were at war.

From a negligible fraction in 1887 the Transvaal's share of world's gold production had risen to 27.6 per cent in 1898, and in the following year came the set-back of the war. Starting with a modest return of 887 oz. in May 1887, the Witwatersrand output reached nearly 8500 oz. in December, making for the eight months a total of 19,080. As more companies came into the active list production rapidly increased and in June 1892, five years after the first declaration, the monthly output for the first time passed the 100,000 mark, an achievement which was fittingly celebrated. The advance was steadily maintained, and in 1898, the last full year before the war interruption, production was nearly 300,000 oz. a month, the total for that year being 3,564,581 oz. of a value of £15,141,376. The average yield was over half an ounce per ton milled, but against this working costs were very high, nearly thirty shillings a ton, due in no small measure to the handicaps of various monopolies granted by the Government, such for instance as that for the supply of dynamite which pressed very heavily on the mines. But no direct taxation of mining profits was introduced until 1898 when a levy of 5 per cent was made. 'This came without any warning to the industry,' stated the Chamber of Mines' report for that year, 'and a protest was at once telegraphed to the Government against the hurried manner in which the measure had been passed', adding that such taxation was, in the opinion of the Chamber, unnecessary.

When war came the industry was giving employment to roughly 10,000 whites and 90,000 natives; its yearly wage bill was about £3,000,000, and on stores the expenditure was approximately £5,000,000, an equal amount being distributed in dividends. These figures make interesting comparison with those of the Transvaal Treasury, whose receipts and expenditure in 1898 each fell a little short of £4,000,000.

At the declaration of war mining work ceased, but the republican government took possession of a few of the properties and mined gold to the value of nearly £3,000,000. Most of the native workers had been repatriated and there was an exodus of the white employees to the Cape and Natal, where a great many volunteered for war service.

VI

The Post-War Expansion—Opening up of the Far East Rand—Geological Contrasts —A Chinese Interlude

Though Johannesburg itself was surrendered to the British forces at the end of May 1900 and the area of occupation was speedily extended, it was a year later before mines could restart crushing and it was not until 1904 that the scale of production before the war was overtaken. Freed of monopolies which had hampered earlier working, but with a tax on profits of 10 per cent imposed in June 1902, the industry showed rapid expansion, particularly when Far East Rand producers came into the field. That expansion was marked by the rise in milling from 3,416,813 tons in 1902 to over 28,000,000 tons in 1916, in production from 1,690,096 to 8,971,359 oz., and in value from £7,179,074 to £38,107,909.

The central area of the Rand had been the scene of the greatest mining activity before the war. The reefs were known then to extend for forty miles or more, but there had been little development in the Far East Rand. On the north-western fringe of that area, later to prove so amazingly rich in its gold content, the New Modderfontein had started milling in 1892 but the early results were not encouraging. At the second annual meeting the chairman announced: 'During the year operations were considerably hampered by an insufficient supply of native labour, by shortness of water, and by a frequent suspension of all ox-wagon transport through the prevalence of rinderpest.' From its 1999 acres of ground the New Modder has since produced gold to the value of nearly £7,000,000 for an expenditure of about £30,000,000 and has distributed to shareholders a sum also in the neighbourhood of £30,000,000. On the southern fringe of the Far East Rand basin the Sub Nigel had commenced operations, but its success was very limited until comparatively recent times when its development reached the astonishingly rich shoots of its northern area. To-day the Sub Nigel, with a working capital of less than £850,000 and a milling basis of only 50,000 tons a month, is operating on a yearly working profit of over £2,000,000 for working expenditure of roughly a million pounds.

Though, as stated earlier, mining had extended to the Far East Rand in the comparatively early days of the fields, the scale of operations there was very restricted, even after the South African War, for it was not until 1914, when other companies had been established and there had been a wide extension of activity, that the wonderful richness of the area became generally recognized.

Geologically the Far East Rand presents a marked

contrast to the Central and Western sections. Here, with the presence of two or more reefs, often in close juxtaposition to each other, mining is carried on at different horizons which naturally add to the working difficulties, but owing to the continuity of the reefs for thousands of feet without interruption high percentages of payability in development are obtained. On the other hand, on the Far East Rand, save for local occurrences, mining is virtually restricted to the Main Reef Leader, the only representative of the Main Reef Group in this area. Against this advantage of simpler working conditions is the fact that, except along the northern margin of the field, where the sheet of conglomerate known as the Main Reef Leader is practically continuous, zones of unpayable ore occur with increasing frequency in a south-westerly direction, so that development drives may have to be carried long distances through unprofitable ground, thus lowering the percentage of payability. A compensating factor is that the gold-bearing patches, or 'shoots' as they are called, frequently attain a length of 2000 feet or more and are of great economic importance. In such a field, however, it is clear that results from exploratory boreholes, more so than in other areas, were always a matter of chance.

Extending as they do over such a wide field, it is not surprising that the Witwatersrand reefs have been subjected to geological disturbances and interruptions marked to-day by a few great regional faults causing displacements of thousands of feet (such as the 'Witpoortje Break' in the west) and by innumerable small breaks and slips which, though unrevealed at the surface, are a frequent source of difficulty in mining. The problem presented in these cases is that of finding the horizon of continuation of the reef, a task that may involve much unprofitable work.

In addition to the Witwatersrand reefs which, because of their economic importance, have received special names, additional reefs are worked wherever their local development warrants it. There is for instance what is frequently called the North Reef, underlying the Main Reef Leader, also there is a group of gold-bearing horizons in the Far East Rand, known collectively as 'Upper Leaders', some of which have proved very consistent over considerable areas.

Even before the South African War the mines had felt the handicap of labour shortage and inquiries had been made as far afield as Sierra Leone, the Gold Coast, and the German dependency of Cameroons regarding possible sources of supply. The results of the investigations were not encouraging. The Government of India did not show any sympathy with the recruitment of labour from the mining districts of that country and the Chamber of Mines did not at that time consider the introduction of Chinese labour advisable. Then there was an offer for the provision of Italian labour, skilled and unskilled, but the scheme would have proved expensive and was not entertained.

The urgent needs of the mines in the expansion

which followed the war led the Crown Colony Government to grant permission for the introduction of Chinese labourers (who had worked well in Australian mines) and the pioneer party arrived in June 1904. Until the repatriation of the last batch in February 1910 altogether 63,000 Chinese coolies were introduced into the Transvaal on three years' indentures under this labour scheme which provided for compulsory repatriation. It was not the first trial with Chinese labourers in this continent, for in November 1892 the Congo Railway Company imported over 600 coolies in its effort to overcome labour difficulties in building the line from the Lower to the Upper Congo. The experiment was disastrous, for within a few months nearly five hundred of the coolies had died and some time after most of the survivors suddenly decamped. A few were subsequently seen far in the interior trying to walk overland to China.

The Witwatersrand experiment was not allowed to have full play, for it had many violent opponents and some of the labourers gave a good deal of trouble. There were numerous desertions and alarm was created in the country districts by murder and pillage. Yielding to the urgent representations of deputations (of one of which General Botha was a member), the Government established police posts at distances of about 500 yards along the Reef to arrest deserters and as a protective measure rifles were issued to farmers.

A touch of comedy was afforded by an incident in military manœuvres at Irene, near Pretoria. The day's operations were well forward. A wood had been shelled by artillery and infantry advanced to the attack. As they approached the position the order to fix bayonets was given, and lines of glittering steel flashed in the sunlight. At this critical moment, to the astonishment of everyone, three Chinamen rushed out of the wood, throwing up their arms in submission. Amazed at the force the Government had brought against them, these deserters realized that the game was up and that surrender was inevitable.

In the mine compounds there were at times serious disorders, and not the least of the evils here was the extensive traffic in opium which the heaviest fines failed to suppress.

It was on the cry of 'Chinese slavery' on the Rand, based on false reports of working conditions, that the Liberals were returned to power in the general election in Britain in 1906. They had made it the chief plank in their platform and election posters represented the Chinamen being led to their work in chains. It was in reply to a question in the House of Commons that Winston Churchill gave to our currency the expression 'terminological inexactitude' as describing the misrepresentation of fact on which the Liberal 'slavery' cry rested.

However, the Liberals had come in and the Chinese had to go. This safeguard was taken in the grant of responsible government, but the Botha administration, established after the first election in 1907, decided against wholesale repatriation; recruiting would cease and the labourers would be sent back to

China as their indentures expired. On February 25th, 1910, the last of the repatriates left. On the preceding day they had exhumed and cremated the bodies of compatriots they had buried, and packed the ashes in a dozen little tea-boxes, neatly nailed down and labelled, to take back to China.

What was to be done with those coolies remaining in the jails of the country? The question was settled between Pekin, London, and Pretoria; Pekin undertaking that if the sentences were commuted in the Transvaal no notice would be taken of them on the return of the men to China. With the individuals most closely concerned the international arrangement was far from popular. Those who had been convicted of housebreaking, a crime much in favour here, pointed out that for such an offence in China they might be decapitated, which went far to explain their reluctance to return. The terms under which they were being surrendered did little to allay their fears, and it was an unwilling and cheerless party of nearly a hundred that set out for China in the company of a strong police escort.

Thus closed a troubled chapter in the Rand's history.

VII

The Strikes of 1913 and 1914—Deportation of Leaders—Influences of the Great War— The Revolt of 1922—A New Advance— The Changing Outlook

For reasons already stated it is not proposed to dwell on the industrial clashes which have furnished some unhappy episodes in the life of the Rand, but no survey, however brief, would be adequate without some record of those struggles. With the merits of particular disputes we need not be concerned—there have been mistakes on both sides—and perhaps we may regard the long immunity from serious trouble that has now been enjoyed as evidence of better understanding and a more sympathetic outlook.

In republican days there were no serious labour difficulties; indeed no labour organization existed until 1892, when a union was formed to resist the proposal of a district magistrate to employ native convict labour in the mines. The convicts did not come and the union had a short life, the balance of funds in hand at the close being worthily voted to the blind mother of a member who had died before the dissolution of the union. A strong miners' organization was established soon after the resumption of mining after the war of 1899-1902 and in May of 1907 a strike was called to resist certain changes in working conditions. It failed in its object, and from this time dates the employment on a large scale of Dutch workers on the mines.

Six years later, in July 1913, labour discontent came to a head in a general strike which grew out of sectional trouble on the New Kleinfontein mine on the East Rand, where the management introduced a change in working hours which deprived some men of their Saturday half-holiday. With the introduction of strike breakers the spread of the strike from mine to mine was accompanied by growing violence, culminating in grave disorders marked by sabotage, incendiarism and bloodshed in Johannesburg on July 4th and 5th. Gunsmiths' shops were looted by rioters— for as an industrial dispute the movement had got completely out of hand—and there were deplorable scenes when military units and police, sniped at from many quarters, carried out orders to fire to clear the streets. In these collisions nineteen persons were killed and many wounded. Among the military and police there was no loss of life but over 150 men were wounded, many seriously. A settlement was negotiated by the Prime Minister, General Botha, and General Smuts, its provisions including the reinstatement of the New Kleinfontein strikers and compensation by the Government of the strike breakers. This compensation was fixed at £300 a head and the amount paid out by the Government was nearly £50,000.

But only six months later, in January 1914, the Witwatersrand was involved in industrial troubles on a much wider scale. Their starting point was a strike on the Natal coalfields followed quickly by a general railway strike in the Union as a protest against retrenchment, directed, it was complained, against trade unionists. The Government mobilized the Defence forces, including Boer commandos, and arrested many of the strike leaders on charges of seditious utterances. The Transvaal Federation of Trades, then in control of the labour organizations, called a general strike on January 13th and the Government replied immediately with a declaration of martial law. Thus the movement was promptly crushed, a closing scene being the 'siege' and surrender on January 15th of the Johannesburg trades hall, where the executive of the federation and a body of their supporters were established behind barricaded doors and windows. Forces of armed police took possession of the surrounding streets, Boer commandos took up threatening positions, and a twelve-pounder gun was trained on the building. But the 'citadel' surrendered without resistance; indeed the 'garrison' of thirty-odd men was unarmed, nor were any arms found inside the building.

Relying on Parliament for an indemnity for its unconstitutional action, the Government deported to England nine strike leaders who were not of South African birth and who were in jail awaiting the for-

mulation of charges against them. Parliament gave
its indemnity in a measure which declared the de-
portees to be undesirables and imposed a ban on their
return. In later years the ban was removed and most
of the men came back to the Union.

Mine natives have a fine record of loyal service, but
there was a wage strike on an extensive scale early in
1920. It broke down through lack of cohesion and
organization, but not before there had been some
unfortunate conflicts with the police.

Gravest and most severe of all Transvaal industrial
conflicts was that of the early part of 1922. It began
on January 1st on the coalfields with resistance to a
wage reduction, and by January 10th it had envel-
oped all the gold mines, the power stations and city
engineering shops. Formal notice had been given by
the Chamber of Mines of certain changes in employment conditions, which would involve a measure of
retrenchment, the Victoria Falls and Transvaal
Power Company had been unable to accede to a re-
quest for wage increases, and in the engineering shops
employees had been notified of a reduction in rates of
pay.

Broadly speaking, the industrial conflict was perhaps an inevitable reaction to influences of the Great
War which had brought its special problems. While
it was necessary to maintain production at the highest
possible level, there was a sharp rise in the cost of
essential supplies, which were difficult to obtain, resulting in a pooling of resources. Many of the employ-

ees volunteered for active service. All could not be allowed to go, but over the war period 5553 men joined the forces and of these 551 laid down their lives. In the working of the industry there was inevitably a loss of efficiency and this influence persisted long after the close of the war. In meeting the greater costs of production the mines were assisted by the suspension of the gold standard in July 1919, which created a currency premium for gold, the price reaching its highest level of 127s. 6d. in February 1920. With the progress of world resettlement the premium steadily decreased and ceased in 1925 on the country's return to the gold standard at the old parity.

In 1921 milling had decreased from the level of over 28,000,000 tons in 1915 and 1916 to less than 23,500,000, production had fallen from nearly 9,000,000 ounces to less than 8,000,000, and the value had declined from £38,000,000 to less than £34,000,000. Working costs had risen from an average of 17s. 1d. per ton in 1914 to 24s. 11d. in December 1921. To the higher level of costs deeper mining had of course in some degree contributed. The difficulties were accentuated by the rapidly vanishing premium on gold which had assisted the mines to meet higher wage scales and the increased cost of stores. Some properties had reached the line of unpayability and many others were perilously close to that position.

The strikes brought paralysis to the gold mines and the collieries; and efforts were made to draw the railway staff into the strife, but without success.

What proved to be a most unfortunate aspect of the struggle was the organization of the strikers on military lines, and before affairs reached a crisis there was scarcely a centre along the Reef without a commando. At first the men were unarmed, but afterwards they paraded with lethal weapons of all descriptions and many later carried rifles, guns and revolvers. As the strike dragged on the dispute to a marked degree lost its industrial character; its leaders preached violence and revolutionary methods, and the personnel of the commandos changed as men of moderate views withdrew and rougher elements were admitted.

The effect of these developments was a series of outrages followed by attacks on police posts, especially at Benoni, which came completely under the control of the strikers' commandos. The Government had insufficient forces to deal with the new situation, and under the proclamation of martial law on March 10th over a wide area citizen forces and burger commandos from the country districts were called out to assist the police in quelling the outbreak. But before these forces could be effectively employed there had been many grave incidents, particularly on the East Rand (where special constables after surrender had been clubbed to death) and in and around Johannesburg. The western suburb of Fordsburg was a citadel of the revolutionaries and here in the closing stages of the drama two of the leaders chose suicide rather than surrender.

There is no need here to describe the operations

which resulted, on March 14th, within four days of the declaration of martial law, in the Government gaining complete control of the situation, and in the restoration of law and order.

The severity of the outbreak will be realized from the heavy casualty roll. Of the military forces and police 72 were killed and 219 wounded; in addition 66 officers and men were admitted to hospital suffering from various injuries. On the civilian side the official classification of casualties showed:

Revolutionaries: Killed or died of wounds 11; wounded or injured 45.

Suspected revolutionaries: Killed or died of wounds 28; wounded or injured 73.

Innocent civilians: Killed or died of wounds 18 Europeans and 24 others; wounded or injured 69 Europeans and 128 others.

With the restoration of law and order early steps were taken for the resumption of mining operations both on the Witwatersrand and in the coalfields, and power stations and engineering shops were soon in normal working.

The reorganization of the gold mining industry prepared the way for a new advance on a sound basis, with a steady increase in production and employment. These were the fruits of industrial peace, and in 1932 production reached the record of 10,987,341 oz., valued at £46,671,258. Milling had risen to about 34,500,000 tons.

In spite of this great achievement, however, the

prosperity of the industry was insecure. Over many years the average yield per ton had been falling because of the reduction of high-grade ore, and in December 1929 the Government Mining Engineer (Dr. Pirow) had estimated that the value of the output (which he anticipated would reach a peak of £43,800,000 in 1932) would fall in twenty years to £10,000,000. The maintenance of the industry was the subject of special investigation by a Low Grade Ore Commission which, in making in 1932 many recommendations designed to assist the mines, formed the estimate that a reduction of working costs by two shillings per ton milled would result in a 50 per cent increase in working life, and a reduction of four shillings per ton in an increase of over 100 per cent.

How pressing was the need for relief is shown by the fact that of thirty-three producers in 1932 one was working at a loss, and six at a profit of under two shillings a ton, the profit in two of these cases being less than a shilling.

And then came the miraculous change in the outlook induced by the suspension of the gold standard, and the sharp rise in the currency price of gold.

VIII

A New Witwatersrand—Effect of Departure from Gold Standard—Local and National Benefits—The Great Expansion

The vision of a Witwatersrand far greater than the boldest optimism had hitherto conceived came into view with the Union's suspension of the gold standard at the end of 1932. That a country depending to an exceptional degree on gold production for its prosperity should gain an immense advantage from a reversion to inconvertible paper is an economic paradox, but in the Union, as elsewhere, suspension of the gold standard implied only recognition of the fact that the national currency was highly overvalued on the existing gold basis, and here, as elsewhere, its true significance has been not in any degree a loss of faith in gold but a determination to control the outflow and protect the national holding.

What the rise in the price of gold from the old statutory level of 85s. an ounce to a sterling value of 140s. has meant to the industry will be best realized if two cardinal points are grasped:

(a) That the Witwatersrand gold deposits consist almost exclusively of extensive low-grade sedimentary beds of which the proportion that can be economically mined increases with the rise in the price of gold, provided of course the rise is not counterbalanced by an advance in working costs.

(b) That with gold at 140s. an ounce and the level of working costs undisturbed, the average pay limit which formerly was in the vicinity of 4.3 dwt. per ton is now approximately 2.9 dwt.; in other words, on a basis of the present average of working costs, and with gold at 85s. an ounce, rock containing less gold than 4.3 dwt. per ton could not be profitably mined, but with gold at 140s. an ounce rock whose gold content is as low as 2.9 dwt. per ton can be mined at a profit.

Another striking presentation of the import of the great change was given in a recent public address by the Government Mining Engineer, Dr. Pirow. Recalling that the Low Grade Ore Commission of 1932 had reached the conclusion that a lowering of working costs by 4s. a ton would double the life of the existing industry, he estimated that an advance in the price of gold from 85s. to 140s., with working costs remaining practically the same, might be said to correspond to a lowering of working costs by about 6s. 6d. a ton, and on this basis the lives of the mines existing in 1932 had, on an average, at a conservative estimate, been increased by well over 150 per cent.

The first great benefit of the change, therefore, was to existing producers, because the rise in the price of gold brought within economic range quantities of ore already developed but hitherto left unmined, not being payable on the old basis, and because the test of the payability of new development was lowered, when the gold price reached 140s. and working costs remained stable, from the old standard of 4.3 dwt. per ton to 2.9 dwt. Therein lies the explanation of the remarkable extension of life to these properties.

But an extension of life was not the whole benefit. At the new level of gold current operations at once became more profitable (a fact which did not escape the attention of the Government), and though there has been a persistent lowering of the grade of ore milled to conform to the average values of the greatly augmented ore reserves, profits remain at a very high level compared with that ruling at the end of 1932. Thus the monthly aggregate of declared estimated working profit for Witwatersrand mines has risen from about £1,250,000 to nearly £3,000,000. In part the advance is due to the great expansion of milling which the new conditions have encouraged, the monthly tonnage having increased from under three millions to over four millions.

The second great effect of a depreciated currency was, for the reasons already given, a wonderful impetus to the opening up of new properties awaiting a favourable opportunity for exploitation, and to exploration in every field which invited examination. Thus within three years, in addition to the great national benefit of the prolongation of the lives of thirty-three established producers, no fewer than fourteen large new mines have been created on the Witwatersrand, and a number of new properties in outside districts hold much promise. On the Far East Rand the opening up of further areas had been to a large extent dependent on the development results on neighbouring properties, a case of following the pay shoots from one property to another. The new outlook changed all that, and there was a wonderful acceleration in the pace of expansion. On the Far West Rand a notable feature of exploration of the past three years has been the prospecting by geophysical methods of vast areas, followed by borehole sinking on a most extensive scale, demonstrating the existence of gold-bearing reefs for a great many miles south-west of Randfontein. In this new field one company (Venterspost) has already been established, a second is on the eve of flotation, and other promotions may be expected to follow, so that the ultimate result may be a wide extension of the area of Witwatersrand production.

The expansion in proved areas has been accompanied by wider exploration on a scale never before witnessed; it has been the grand opportunity of putting finally to the test all theories, plausible or of any other class, regarding Witwatersrand reef extensions, near or remote; and when the horizons have been cleared we shall emerge from the great adventure with much joy and sadness—but in what proportions, who shall say?

Closely linked with the other major developments has been the abundance of money, allied with an all-pervading spirit of optimism, resulting in the creation of such an opportunity for new capital issues as is never likely to recur, and indeed may never again be required. Because of the great rise in share values on the higher basis of profit, working companies have been able by high share premiums to finance advantageous programmes of expansion with only moderate issues of additional capital, and new enterprises have also been able to place their share issues at substantial premiums, an incalculable advantage in these days of deep mining and heavy capital requirements. The position too has been exploited to the full by companies of the most speculative character whose fortunes, and those of their promoters, have depended on the success of share market activities rather than on the results of drilling and shaft sinking. Here too has been the realization that such an opportunity would probably never again present itself, and with a public ready and willing to pay it is perhaps not surprising that it was not neglected.

Share dealings grew to record volumes. With each sharp rise in the price of gold the flood of orders rose, and even with a rush of new admissions and with staffs increased to the limits of accommodation, brokers were often quite unable to cope with the day's business, though clerks worked on until the early morning hours. Some idea of the great expansion is conveyed by the fact that the market value of the stocks of gold and finance companies, old and new, with a nominal capital of about £75,000,000 at the end of 1932, rose in a few months from less than £125,000,000 to over £350,000,000. It was Johannesburg's greatest and most sustained boom, which drew into share dealing people who had never before dabbled in the market. But Johannesburg was not alone in the business. London was always a heavy dealer, often giving the lead in share movements, and Throgmorton Street at times provided scenes of the wildest excitement. Setbacks were inevitable, and were not long in being realized, a sobering influence being exercised by taxation announcements and the steady adjustment of the grade of ore milled to the lower average values of the greatly augmented ore reserves. Though the tide of speculation frequently carried shares over their true values, South African gold mining stocks became an increasingly attractive investment because of the greatly increased profits, the extended life of the industry, and the general cheapness of money.

The expansion of the industry has been of true benefit to labour, for employment has increased from under 23,500 whites and 220,000 natives in December 1932 to about 33,000 whites and 300,000 natives at the end of 1935. The position of white workers too has been considerably enhanced by the creation of a provident fund wholly sustained by the employers, by new and more liberal holiday leave regulations unequalled elsewhere in the mining world, and by the payment of a holiday bonus of £3 8s. per week of leave.

From the national point of view, the benefit of the new mining prosperity and the great expansion of operations has been incalculable. An accumulated deficit of over £2,000,000 was converted in 1933-4 to a surplus of £4,500,000. Despite remission of general taxation to the extent of £2,000,000, the Budget of 1934-5 showed another surplus of almost £2,500,000, and notwithstanding a further surrender of revenue an even greater surplus on the working for 1935-6 has been realized. The State railway budgets too have staged a spectacular recovery. Moreover, the prosperity of the gold mining industry has enabled the Government to save agriculture from the disaster which threatened from the sustained depression of world commodity prices, and on various schemes of rehabilitation expenditure in three years has approached £25,000,000.

Taxation has fallen heavily on the mines and in its application has produced many inequities which called for revision. While on the one hand it has provoked the strongest condemnation, there have also been ill-informed critics of another class who consider it has been inadequate. Into a discussion of the ethics of the taxation measures however we need not be drawn.[1]

---

[1] In 1936 there has been a welcome simplification of taxation. The income tax has been reduced from 20 to 15 per cent, and the excess profits duty and surtax have been replaced by a formula based on the ratio of taxable income to revenue, designed to maintain the Government's participation in profits on the former scale.

PART THREE

An Introduction to Technical and other
Aspects of a great Industry

I

A Geological Guide—How the Reefs Divide

Few people who put their money into gold shares realize what a wide variation there is in the distribution of reefs on the Witwatersrand. Particularly in boom times, when news of 'good things' spreads like perfect radio transmission with no disturbance from atmospherics, there is an amazing readiness to believe that main reefs are everywhere, only awaiting capital to develop them; and the process of disillusionment has often been sad and costly.

The main Witwatersrand conglomerate beds lie at four or five different horizons and are known respectively as the Main, Livingstone, Bird, Kimberley, and Elsburg series of reefs.

In the Main Reef Group are three principal bands of conglomerate, the Main Reef, Main Reef Leader, and South Reef. In the characteristics of these reefs there are wide dissimilarities. Thus in the Main Reef the pebbles are of uniform average size, with no well-marked grading. On the other hand, in the Main Reef Leader, not only is there very commonly a considerable range in the size of pebbles but also a marked graded arrangement; further there is frequently such a strong tendency to concentration that the larger pebbles, found at the foot of the reef, are not infrequently associated with 'visible' gold and extraordinarily high assays. So marked are the pebble characteristics of the Main Reef Leader that frequently it would be possible to say, in the examination of a block comprising the whole thickness, which was the original upper and lower side of the specimen; such determination could rarely be made with a similar block of Main Reef. The South Reef shows considerable variation; in some localities it presents resemblances to the Main Reef Leader. The Main Reef and the Main Reef Leader are usually very closely associated, forming on portions of the Central Rand practically a single large body of conglomerate.

All three reefs of the group, the Main Reef, Main Reef Leader, and South Reef, are present in the Central Rand, but while the Main and South Reefs persist into the Far West, the Main Reef Leader dies out before reaching that area. On the other hand the Main and South Reefs die out in an easterly direction, leaving the Main Reef Leader as the only representative of the trinity in the Far East Rand.

The Livingstone Reefs (or Livingstone series) lie above the Main Reef Group. As a rule the amount of gold associated with the pebbly bands is small and the reefs have not been shown to be of much economic importance.

Passing upwards in the formation, next in order come the Bird Reefs, a group very persistent throughout the whole extent of the Rand. In the west-central and western portions the Bird Reefs frequently contain a moderate amount of gold and in one area have proved to be of considerable value.

In the Kimberley reefs, distributed through a thickness of beds of 700 feet or more, the individual pebble beds are very numerous. The reefs are most strongly developed on the west-central and western portions of the Rand.

The Elsburg reefs, usually very conspicuous at the surface in the central Rand, especially immediately to the south of Johannesburg, are not of much value. Some of the earliest pioneer development was on these reefs.

Other geological formations in the Witwatersrand area include the Ventersdorp system, the Transvaal system, and the Karroo system. The Ventersdorp system plays but a small part in the mining area, but in the Transvaal system is the Black Reef Series, whose feature is the frequent occurrence, in association with the quartzites, of one or more bands of conglomerate usually very dark in colour. These conglomerates, usually to some extent auriferous, have been mined in a few places where they attain sufficient thickness accompanied by a correspondingly large gold content. The values are, however, very patchy.

Also in the Transvaal system is the dolomite series containing considerable accumulations of water. The extensive area of dolomite country lying to the south of the Rand was for long the main source of water supply to Johannesburg and other Reef townships. In the Far East Rand (and in the Far West Rand) large areas of the Witwatersrand system are overlaid by dolomite, adding frequently to the difficulties of shaft-sinking operations.

Coal measures form part of the Karroo system, and in the early days of the Rand the coal mines in the Boksburg area were an important factor in the development of the goldfields. They were later superseded by other sources of supply, farther east, yielding coal of a superior quality, but the occurrence of workable coal seams in the immediate locality of important gold deposits, so that the workings of one may exist above the other, has been stated to be almost unique in the history of mining.

II

The Conquest of Depth—Shaft Developments — The Problem of Ventilation — Support of Working Places

As we have seen, mining on the Rand did not start on any systematic basis; no one knew to what depths the reefs extended. Nor has that point been determined to-day after fifty years of mining. But when it was ascertained by deep cuts and trenches that the deposit did continue in depth and value, systematic mining began, a lead being given at Langlaagte where in 1887 four inclined shafts were sunk on the reef to a depth of sixty feet and connected by a level about 1200 feet long. Early in 1888 several vertical shafts were started and at the end of 1889 began the system of sinking large inclines to act as main shafts, thus doing away with numerous small ones. Inclined shafts were practical for operations on the outcrop, but for companies on the dip side of others vertical shafts had to be sunk. Levels at first were sixty to one hundred feet apart, but as depths increased these steadily increased and to-day, especially where the dip is very gradual, levels may be one thousand feet or more apart. The ground in these pioneer levels was blocked out on the same lines as followed to-day, and in this practice we see the beginning of the ore reserve system on which rests the stability of the industry to-day. As the reef was followed down, vertical shafts turned to compound shafts, changing their dip from vertical to inclined, or from steep to flat dips.

Engineering problems grew more formidable as ground was proved farther and farther away from the line of outcrop, for vertical shafts had to go deeper to reach the reef horizons which had to be determined by borehole drilling. Engineering science triumphed over the problems presented, but a few short years ago there seemed to be general recognition that the limits of direct hoisting set by engineering and other considerations had been reached at a depth of 4500 feet, though at Randfontein a vertical shaft wind of 4755 feet had been installed. The system of stage hoisting was then instituted and developed to reach deposits lying beyond this depth, a new shaft, vertical or inclined, being started in the vicinity of the bottom of the original shaft, at which point hoisting machinery had of course to be installed. On the old Village Deep (now incorporated in the Robinson Deep), where the workings have penetrated to a vertical depth of 8500 feet, the boreholes put down 8600 feet from the outcrop struck the South Reef at a depth of 4801 feet and the Main Reef Leader at 4878 feet. The vertical shaft was sunk to a depth of 4200 feet and the reefs were then reached by a sub-incline shaft, hoisting

Interior of Winding Engine House. The winding drum is one of the largest on the fields, and in the world. Note the man standing in front of the plant and the steps leading to the operator's station.

being done in two stages. For still deeper working further sub-inclines were sunk so that three-stage hoisting was introduced. The Village Deep took up the reefs on the dip from the Village Main Reef, which in turn had taken up the ground on the dip side of the outcrop mine, the Jubilee. The story of the progress from outcrop to the world's deepest level is thus illustrated in the successive development of these three mining areas.

Within the past few years there has been a remarkable increase in the depth of single lift winding due to improved machinery, automatic braking, better ropes and the use of skips and cages of duralumin or similar alloy. Equipments are being installed for direct lifts up to 6600 feet (a mile and a quarter) and a depth of 6800 feet is even contemplated. The reduction of stage winding is of course of the utmost economic importance and ultra-deep shafts achieve this object. In some cases at present, with the gradual development of winding as the reef was followed in depth, third and even fourth-stage winding has been found necessary.

With the steady progress to depth hoisting equipment has necessarily undergone great changes. Light 10-cwt. skips were useful enough in shallow pioneer shafts and in the days of the small steam engine, but they were toy appliances compared with the giant, high-speed, electrically operated hoists of to-day. One of the latest of these has been installed to lift with a two-inch rope a rock load of eight tons from a vertical depth of 6300 feet in a skip weighing

9000 lb. with a winding speed of 3000 feet a minute.

Such great advances have been made possible by the provision of an abundant supply of electrical power. Its development on a large scale began about 1906, and the story of its expansion is a record hardly less arresting than that of the development of the gold industry itself. The use of steam has largely been abandoned in favour of electrical power and compressed air. Without these aids the industry could never have reached its present standard of efficiency and millions of ounces of gold now being recovered would have remained beyond reach. The use of steam had set very definite limits to mining depths. Stage hoisting, an essential stage of development, was made possible only by the employment of electrical power, transmitted from surface plant. Steam hoists require boilers and other adjuncts and their use underground is clearly impracticable.

Another of the great problems which faced engineers with mining at increasing depths has been that of ventilation of workings. With a comparatively flat temperature gradient of 1 deg. F. for every 200 feet of vertical depth, the provision of adequate cooling arrangements would not ordinarily have proved very difficult, but in the war against silicosis-producing dust so much water has to be used that the mine air becomes saturated and loses much of its cooling value. Large volumes of fresh air are therefore necessary. The problem has been met by the installation of great ventilating fans, some of them the largest in the

Sub-haulage station in a Witwatersrand mine. This picture should be studied in the light of the fact that the station is over 4,000 feet below the surface.

world, and shafts have been sunk at heavy cost solely for ventilation purposes. In addition to main ventilating fans, subsidiary fans are installed to split air currents and supply the working places with pure air. It will be seen therefore that, apart from any other considerations, the question of mining at even greater depths than those now reached must depend, in great measure, on the progress of air cooling science. On the Robinson Deep with its workings reaching down to 8500 feet, a surface air cooling plant has been installed to produce for the mine workings a cooling equivalent to some 2000 tons of ice a day. It is calculated that workings, say, at 7500 feet will thus be set back to normal temperature conditions at 6000 feet. At other mines alternative methods of air cooling, based on the use of devaporized compressed air, have been adopted. The results of these experiments should answer the question whether still deeper mining is humanly practicable.

Yet another great and continuing problem in the conquest of depth is that of the support of working places. Engineering science has been faced with no more formidable task than this, for to the normal factors of rock stresses has been added that of earth tremors due, according to best scientific opinion, to the shattering of mine pillars, to the fracture of strata overlying excavated areas, or to the settling of strata into and over the excavation. The means adopted for support of working places has undergone many changes as the problem itself has changed with depth.

To-day the methods in use represent a change-over from hanging support to hanging control designed to safeguard workers at the faces for a sufficient time to extract the ore and subsequently to let down the hanging wall without violence.

These are the greatest problems that deep mining has presented, but many other difficulties have had to be overcome, such for instance as those associated with underground haulage, with the handling of ore in stopes, and with the disposal of enormous quantities of water under pressure from fissures, a complication which has involved heavy expenditure on pumping equipment.

The Witwatersrand industry has every reason to be proud of its great engineering achievements and its many notable contributions to mining science.

III

Ore Reserves and their Valuation—Effect of Currency Depreciation

The stability of the Witwatersrand gold mining industry rests on its ore reserves (which we may speak of as the mining stock-in-trade) and the established reliability of the system of their calculation. Ore reserves are not a balance sheet item, and are scarcely liquid assets, but may be classed as 'fixed deposits', deposits certainly, and fixed until they are removed by drill and dynamite. A very solid guarantee for the future, they are not of course the measure of a mine's life, unless development has come to an end through exhaustion of ground, but they represent the tonnage developed in advance of the mill. Thus ore reserves do not consist of rock already mined, brought to the surface, and neatly packed ready for milling; they are the blocks of ore in the mine sufficiently opened up by development for their value to be determined with a fair degree of accuracy and their tonnage reliably estimated. When bodies of ore have been made available for mining by shafts and by drives connected by winzes (down) and raises (up), samples are taken at regular intervals (usually five feet) round the blocks in accordance with well-established methods. The standard practice is to chip off as fair a sample from each band as will weigh from two to five pounds, this being the amount most convenient for the assayer. As each sample is taken it is placed in a bag with a card bearing its reference number (for all sampling is methodically planned) and the bag, sealed, is sent to the assayer who, after crushing, assays two portions to find how much gold they contain. If the two results disagree very materially the lower one is taken. The assayer expresses his findings as the number of penny-weights of gold that could be extracted from a ton of rock similar to that in the bag. From the assays of the samples estimates are made of the value of the blocks as a whole, the tonnage being calculated on the stop-ing width, that is the width to be mined out in actual working. The stoping width, governed by the width of the reef or reefs, and other factors, varies in Rand mines from twenty-eight inches (where the reef is very narrow but of high value) to six feet or more (where the reef is generally in bands separated by barren rock). Reef values are commonly expressed in inch-pennyweights, the product of the stoping width in inches multiplied by the value in penny-weights.[1] The inch-dwt. figure gives a ready index of payability, for to arrive at the value per ton it is only necessary to divide the inch-dwts. by the stoping width. Thus with gold at 140s. an ounce fine (7s. a pennyweight), working costs at 21s. a ton (to take a

[1] In development results the inch-dwt. given is frequently the reef width multiplied by the value.

convenient figure) would be equivalent to 3 dwt. With a stoping width of 60 inches, 180 inch-dwt. would be below the pay limit as the theoretical yield (180 divided by 60) would be only 3 dwt. per ton which would be absorbed in working costs. But if the reef formation were such that the stoping width were only 30 inches the yield would be 6 dwt. (180 divided by 30), thus representing high payability.

In the estimates of ore reserves the practice is not to take the full assay values of samples but to make a reduction (generally about 10 per cent), an adjustment which in actual working experience has been found desirable. Other adjustments in the direction of conservatism are also made.

In cases where gold is more or less evenly distributed, the method of calculating the value of a block of ground is to develop and sample the rock on all four sides (or on three sides where the fourth is on dyke or fault), but where the gold lies in well-defined shoots it is possible to calculate the value of a block if it has been developed only on top and bottom and a connection made through the centre of the shoot.

Sound mining practice dictates that the value of the rock mined from ore reserves should bear a close relation to the average value of the ore reserve blocks, any deviation above that figure being regarded as overmining and below as undermining. Government leases embody safeguards against either practice. In all cases however a portion (in old mines a considerable portion) of the tonnage milled comes from outside the ore reserves, e.g. development rock, reclamation and sweeping tonnage, etc. Blocks of ground which are found to be below the pay limit are of course excluded from the ore reserve tonnage.

The rise in the currency price of gold which followed the Union's abandonment of the gold standard at the end of 1932 brought immense tonnages of developed and hitherto unpayable ground within the new pay limits, and correspondingly the payability of new development greatly increased.

IV

Silicosis and the Cost—The Success of Combative Measures

In the development of the Witwatersrand gold mining industry, silicosis, or miner's phthisis, as it is commonly termed, has taken heavy toll, but happily the energetic preventive measures taken have met with great success and the liability of the working miner to contract the disease has been progressively reduced to a marked degree. In a recent public address the Government Mining Engineer stated: 'Although the problem has not been solved we are steadily gaining ground, and if our past rate of progress is maintained we shall within a reasonable time reduce the risk to comparatively minor proportions.'

Miner's phthisis is a chronic disease of the lungs due to more or less continuous inhalation, over long periods, of fine dust. All true cases are primarily cases of silicosis and in the later stages tuberculosis becomes commonly or invariably superimposed upon this condition.

It was shortly after the South African War of 1899-1902 that the existence of silicosis became known and preventive steps were first taken, but the gravity of the problem was not fully realized until 1912. From that year dates the legal provision for compensation for sufferers and the initiation of systematic and vigorous methods of control. Stringent regulations require the use of water to prevent the escape of dust at its source and other preventive measures include defined standards and methods of ventilation, the single shift system, the restriction of blasting operations to once in twenty-four hours, the regulation of methods of blasting, and the arrangement of working conditions to secure the least possible exposure of workers to dust and fumes.

These safeguards are based primarily on the recommendations of the Miner's Phthisis Prevention Committee, a strong body fully representative of the Department of Mines and the mining industry appointed in 1912, whose report, published in 1916, has been described as a landmark in the development of preventive measures against silicosis. And research in this matter of such vital importance to the worker and the industry goes on ceaselessly. Recently, a Silicosis Research Advisory Committee, representative of all organizations concerned, was created, and the Chamber of Mines has called in the assistance of an outstanding authority on dust problems to devote his time to experimental research work in the pursuit of still greater improvements in the dust condition of mine air.

In 1916 the Government established the Miners' Phthisis Medical Bureau, an appointment which marked a new departure in industrial hygiene. It is a central body composed of whole-time Government medical officers whose main functions are to conduct an initial examination of all newcomers to the industry (who may not be employed without the bureau's 'red ticket'), an examination of each working miner once every six months for the early detection of all cases of silicosis or tuberculosis, and a benefits examination of all claimants for compensation. There are also initial and periodical examinations of natives conducted by mine medical officers acting as examiners under the Act.

The initial examination has resulted in the gradual introduction of men of specially selected physique, referred to in the bureau reports as 'new Rand miners', who now form the greater proportion of the force employed. The periodical examination presents the opportunity for detection and immediate removal of all persons suffering from tuberculosis, or tuberculosis with silicosis, an important feature of preventive policy.

The law defines three stages of silicosis—ante-primary, primary, and secondary. For the first two stages lump sum compensation is paid; for the third, where capacity for work has been seriously and permanently impaired, the compensation is a monthly life pension with allowance for wife, and children under sixteen years of age.

The main production of past and current cases of phthisis has been among underground employees in the service of the gold mines before 1916, and the latest figures available bearing on the human toll of the disease and the monetary cost are those contained in the annual report of the Miners' Phthisis Board, which administers the compensation funds, for the year ended March 31st, 1935. This shows that up to that date 3306 miners who had been granted secondary awards had died and the average of their life from the date of the bureau's certificate was 4.05 years. Pensions were being paid to 1777 miners, and additional allowances to 1312 wives and 2309 children. Allowances were also being paid to 5673 dependents of miners who had died.

To provide the funds for compensation the law makes an annual levy on mines scheduled under the Act. This levy has reached the sum of £800,000 and the contributions have reached an aggregate of over £17,000,000. Up to the end of March 1935 the Board had paid out over £15,250,000 in awards to miners and dependents, and to native labourers over £1,000,000. The outstanding liability of the scheduled mines was capitalized early in 1935 at £11,500,000, for which annual provision, based on the estimated lives of the companies responsible, has to be made.

These are big figures, but the industry does not allow its monetary liabilities as created by legislation to set a limit to its concern for silicotics. For many years the Chamber of Mines has, in co-operation with the Government, maintained sanatoria for advanced sufferers, and an organized effort is made to secure suitable employment, on the mines or elsewhere, for men not physically incapacitated.

V

How the Ore is Won from the Depths— Recovery of the Gold—The Metallurgical Achievement

The minting of gold having virtually ceased,[1] the business of gold production to-day may be concisely expressed as that of transferring the metal from one fastness to another—from the vaults of the earth to the vaults of the world's banks.

How is the gold won from the depths and by what processes is it prepared for reburial? Within the compass of this small volume it is not possible to do more than convey a general idea of the various stages; any comprehensive description would necessarily have to deal not only with the main processes but with the many intermediate steps of an intricate technical character.

A mine, as you know, is opened up by shaft sinking and drives and then by the blocking out of ore bodies by raises and winzes connecting the levels. In devel-

[1] A branch of the Royal Mint was established at Pretoria in 1923 'with a view to the possible coinage annually of a large proportion of the gold output of the Rand mines'. No provision was made there for the refining of gold bullion, this process being undertaken at the Rand Refinery at Germiston.

opment the mechanical drill is the spearhead of attack and when the day's drilling is completed in a stope (the name given to the working place where ore is being mined) the holes made by drilling are charged with explosives which, after the working party has been withdrawn, are fired by the miner in charge whose anxious duty it is to count the reports as the charges explode to satisfy himself that there have been no misfires. Drilling into a misfired hole, or even perhaps near one, means disaster. After fuller examination of the working face the following morning for misfires, the ore broken in the explosions is cleared from the stope to the level below, the stope is made safe by supports, etc., is watered down, and drilling is resumed. The broken ore is conveyed by mechanical haulage along the levels to the shaft bins, loaded into skips, and raised to the surface.

In the surface operations will be found much divergence of practice, because milling and metallurgical science has necessarily been progressive and some of the older producers have not found it economically attractive to replace existing plant representing heavy capital expenditure by new equipment. Rather has the tendency been to harness modern invention, when practicable, to established machinery, as in the use of the tube mill in association with the old stamp mill. Ore at the surface had been fairly free milling because of its oxidization and the natural concentration of its gold content, but at depth the gold is imprisoned in pyritic, or sulphide, rock, which has presented far more difficult problems of recovery.

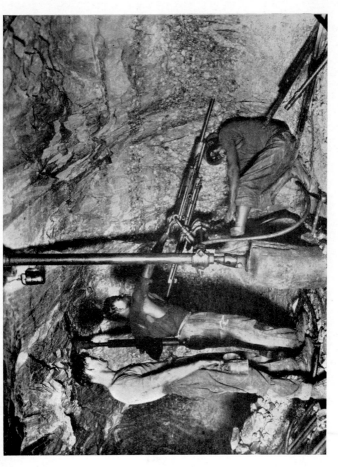

Thousands of feet below the surface. Drillers at work in a particularly well-defined section of banket reef.

Hammer and jumper were the first implements of attack in the hands of native drillers in the Rand mines—all through the piece drilling has been the task of natives—but as the depth of mining increased and the rock became harder to work more effective methods of breaking the ore had to be employed. We see mechanical drills introduced, first for development work in the driving of tunnels and then for the actual mining of ore, but they were cumbersome machines weighing from 300 to 400 lb. which required special mounting, in itself work for two natives. The fast-expanding scale of mining demanded more efficient aids, and to encourage the production of a drill suitable for local conditions the Chamber of Mines inaugurated a stope drill competition in 1908. Twenty-three manufacturers submitted entries for the substantial prizes offered. Though the immediate results were disappointing (even the winning drill did not prove a success in practice) interest was stimulated to such a degree that there was a marked and rapid improvement in drill design leading eventually to the universal adoption of a light drill known as the 'jackhammer', weighing only 50 lb. complete and thus extremely mobile. Worked by compressed air, it can be operated by one person and its use has made it possible to substitute machine drilling for hand drilling in narrow workings and in places where the employment of large machines would be impracticable. In these narrow stopes the operator usually lies on his back and supports the machine by foot, in this way also exerting the necessary pressure on the machine and the advancing drill.

The substitution of machine drilling for hand drilling resulted in a great economy of labour, for a large number of natives previously employed on drilling were thereby liberated for other work. It was thus another important landmark in the advance of mining.

In the evolution of metallurgical practice the old familiar stamp mill has lost its once proud position. Time was when the stamp was considered indispensable; certainly so in the earlier days of the fields when it was the only known method of crushing. Then it held imperious sway, for, as will be recalled, in pioneer mining all ore had to be taken to the mills which were often miles away; they did not stand near the shaft heads waiting to be fed. The stamp indeed held its supremacy until the extension of the cyanide process to the treatment of slime which had hitherto been allowed to run to waste as no method of recovering its gold content had been discovered. The stamp mill had the merit of producing only a small amount of slime but this factor became of less importance when slime no longer represented a waste product.

The earliest stamps weighed only about 500 lb. or even less, but the weight was steadily increased, particularly after the introduction in 1904 of the tube mill, which to a great extent relieved the stamp of the necessity for fine grinding and enabled it, with coarser screening, to increase its crushing duty. Stamps of 2000 lb. and over were then employed.

Within two years of the start of mining operations on the Rand the number of stamps running was nearly 700. They reached a maximum of 9554 in 1912 including the Randfontein battery of 600 stamps, the biggest mill under one roof in the world. Five years later, however, the number had fallen by about 4000 because, with improving efficiency, the tube mill became increasingly important in the milling circuit and it became practicable, in modern reduction plants, to dispense not only with stamps but also with sand treatment units, thus effecting a big capital saving. A crusher-tube-mill all-sliming plant capable of treating 50,000 tons a month costs approximately £300,000, against £400,000 for a plant of similar capacity with stamps and sand treatment equipment.

The stamp however will die hard, for though it is now excluded from modern mills it has yet to be demonstrated that it would be profitable for mines to replace existing stamps with crushers and tube mills. In fact in the last few years there has been a slight increase in the number of stamps in use, due to the activities of small companies.

In the preliminary stages reduction practice to-day is more or less uniform. The ore is first screened so that the fines may go direct to the mills. The larger ore is washed and the waste rock sorted out, a practice first adopted in 1892. This duty is performed by natives standing on each side of a travelling belt carrying the ore to the crushers, and the waste rock is sent to dumps. The powerful crushers reduce the ore to convenient size for the stamps or tube mills. Stamps, which may weigh up to 2000 lb., operate about one hundred times a minute with an average drop of eight inches. At one time they were the sole grinding unit, but now they are required to do only the coarser grinding and the finer grinding is done by tube mills. In modern plants the stamp mill has been excluded and the grinding is done wholly by tube mills in two or sometimes three stages, with classification of the pulp after each. This is the process known as 'all-sliming' and it dispenses with the necessity for separate treatment of sand and slime. Tube mills are mostly 6 feet 6 inches in diameter by 20 feet in length, but some measure 8 feet by 16 feet. They are steel cylinders which are half filled with pebbles or a combination of pebbles and steel balls which, when the mill is rotated, fall upon the partly crushed rock and reduce it to the required degree of fineness. The pebbles are not the sort you may collect on the seashore; they are lumps of rock selected from the mine ore.

Up to about 60 per cent of the gold content of the ore is freed by milling, and the old method of recovery was the use of amalgam plates over which the mill pulp flowed thinly, the released particles of gold being held by the mercury on the plates. It was a process with serious disadvantages, the lock-up of gold on the plates, the possibility of loss by theft, and the possibility of mercurial poisoning of workmen. In place of amalgamation plates, corduroy concentration is now in general use; in one or two cases, where milling is done in a cyanide solution instead of water, amalgamation has been done away with altogether in favour of total recovery in the cyanide treatment section of the plant.

In corduroy concentration the mill product flows over an area of corduroy on which the concentrate containing the free gold is held. Every four hours the concentrate is removed from the blankets, and the daily supply collected in this way over twenty-four hours is reduced to about half by pressing and charged into barrels, the tailing from this process passing back into the milling circuit. The amalgam obtained from the barrel, after the excess of mercury has been removed by treatment with compressed air. assays about 40 per cent of gold; the barrel residue, after separation of the amalgam, assays several ounces to the ton and is either fed into the milling circuit or is ground intensively fine and cyanided separately. Before this is done, however, the residue is run over a small corduroy table for the collection of osmiridium, of which over 5000 ounces, in value roughly £30,000, is recovered yearly. The amalgam is accumulated for some days and is then retorted, the mercury recovered by distillation being re-used in the barrels. The sponge gold resulting from the retorting process is then cast into bars.

We have been dealing so far with the recovery of the gold freed in milling. Let us now follow the progress of the pulp from the mills. Except in the all-sliming plants, which number about one quarter of all the reduction plants on the Rand and where the pulp goes to the cyanide treatment section without classification, the mill product usually gravitates to cones which separate the sand from the slime; the sand goes to the huge collecting tanks and the slime gravitates to slime collectors for settlement. The sand is led either with water or a cyanide solution; if with a cyanide solution the treatment may be completed in the tanks. Where there are no classifiers for separating the sand and slime, as is the case with some of the older plants, the mill pulp goes into the sand collector, the sand remaining and the slime escaping through discharge gates to the slime collectors. If the cyanide process is not carried out in the collectors, the collected sand is drained and transferred to tanks where it is subjected to treatment with cyanide solutions over a period of from four to seven days, the period depending on the capacity of the plant. As aeration is essential for dissolving the gold, the sand is allowed to drain dry as frequently as possible between pumpings to permit the entry of air. When, after the final solution, the sand has again been drained dry, it is conveyed by endless rope haulage to the sand residue dumps which have risen to such great heights from one end of the Witwatersrand to the other and dominate the landscape.

From the sand and slime classifiers the slime gravitates to slime collectors for settlement. Usually in cyanide solution, the thickened slime is then conveyed to tanks for cyanide treatment. Depending on such factors as the nature of the ore, the degree of grinding, and the percentage of ore treated as slime, the

Sentinels of the Reef: A typical mine dump on the Witwatersrand.
Photo by staff photographer of The Star.

time required for dissolving the gold varies from four to twenty-four hours. Either by decantation (as in a few of the older plants) or by vacuum filtration, the gold-bearing solution is separated from the treated slime which is then pumped into slime dams, the disposal of the slime in this way being dictated by the topography of the Rand. Several dams have reached a height of over one hundred feet and on some properties the provision of areas for slime dams is becoming a difficult problem. Sand from the dump may be used for refilling in mine supports, but no one seems to have any further use for the slime.

While a sufficiency of oxygen is necessary to ensure maximum dissolution of gold in both sand and slime treatment, it is equally important that oxygen is absent from the solutions from which the gold is afterwards precipitated, for if oxygen is present the product is low grade, difficult and expensive to smelt. In the dissolution process therefore the solutions are supplied with dissolved oxygen, and in precipitation the solutions are de-oxygenated. The solutions too must be free from suspended matter and for this purpose all the slime solution is passed through sand clarifiers, the sand leachings being usually sufficiently clear.

Precipitation is achieved on the majority of the older plants by the zinc shaving method, but zinc dust precipitation is the newer and more general process. Zinc shavings are packed evenly into wooden or steel boxes divided into five compartments, the solution passing from one compartment to another and so on right through the box. About once a fortnight the zinc is washed to free the gold loosely adhering and the finely broken zinc shavings which, after removal, are treated with sulphuric acid. By this means the zinc is dissolved and the gold is concentrated. After washing, the gold slime is filter-pressed and the filter cake is sent to the smelting department after being dried with compressed air. In the more widely employed method of zinc dust precipitation, the zinc dust is added to the solution after de-aeration and the solution then goes to a circular vat in which about thirty-two leaves, four feet by six feet, are suspended. The leaves consist of a framework of perforated iron piping covered with sheets of canvas. The zinc-gold slime is deposited on the canvas and the clean filtrate passes through, carrying only a trace of gold. The gold slime is washed off the canvas leaves at periods of ten or fifteen days, is acid-treated in another vat, and sent to the smelting department after being washed and filtered.

In the smelting house, after various impurities have been removed, the gold is melted down into crucibles and cast into bar moulds ready for refining.

The bullion averages about 88 per cent fine gold. From the mines it is sent to the industry's refinery at Germiston, where the refining is done by the chlorine process. The average fineness of the gold produced is 995.6, and of silver, which is in the bullion in the proportion of roughly one to ten, 998.3.

The gold output is marketed by agreement through the medium of the S.A. Reserve Bank, acting in co-operation with the Bank of England, and the Reserve Bank thus maintains control over the exchange position, shipping gold for sale abroad as may be required to meet all demands for exchange however they may arise.

VI

The Modern Mine—Where the First Millions Go—The Long Road to Production

Before an ounce of gold can be produced by a new mine on the Witwatersrand to-day, roughly two million pounds will have to be spent; in other words, two millions will be the cost of the first ounce of gold recovered, a startling contrast with the days when reefs were lying at the surface and companies could start operations with a capital of a few thousand pounds. The cost may well be more, depending on the depth of the deposits and the progress of development; there have been many flotations with far greater capital equipment.

When operations began on the fields the job of opening up a property was primarily that of the mining engineer, or even perhaps of the practical miner. But before the responsibility of the mining engineer begins to-day, as the Government Mining Engineer emphasized in a recent address, aerial survey of the ground may be required to gain information regarding the boundaries of different geological strata, faults and dykes, and their correlation, and a geologist may have to employ several if not all of the latest methods of geophysical prospecting for guidance as to the position and depth of mineral deposits and structural features. If these investigations are encouraging in their results and calculations, there must be patient borehole work to determine the reef horizons and the best positions for shaft sinking.

Borehole drilling is beset with many difficulties, of which not the least is the tendency of the drill to diverge from its course at depth. In the Rand field a case is on record of a borehole showing a measurement of 6600 feet along the rods but with a vertical depth of only 4813 feet. Its inclination at the bottom was 36 degrees to the horizontal and its horizontal displacement was 3632 feet from the mouth of the hole. When boreholes intersect the reef they may reveal good or poor values, but in neither case can these results be accepted as a guide to the value of the property; that can only be established by later development. With the information gained the mining engineer must satisfy himself that the necessary tonnages and values are likely to be present, for values without tonnages are as valueless as tonnages without values, and then he must plan the layout of the mine in co-operation with mechanical and electrical engineers, metallurgists, chemists, surveyors, medical experts (who will be concerned with the steps to be taken to ensure the safety and health of the workers), accountants, etc. The layout of a mine is a great responsibility, for a miscalculation or even an error in judgment may involve a large amount of unnecessary capital expenditure or, through misguided savings in initial capital expenditure, add thousands of pounds to annual costs.

Most of the modern mines will require a period of four, five or even more years of development and construction before the production stage can be reached. Shafts must be sunk to the reef horizon perhaps several thousand feet deep, working places must be opened up and ore blocked out, reduction works established, and all the other customary provision made before there can be any thought of production.

Shaft sinking, for which a period of eighteen months to two years is required, costs from £30 to £50 a foot, so that two shafts sunk to a depth of 5000 feet might well cost £500,000; two shafts are necessary unless connection has been established with a neighbouring mine. In dolomite areas particularly, there are serious water difficulties to be overcome which retard advance and increase the cost.

The outlay on shaft sinking does not of course complete the bill on this vital feature of development, for shafts must be equipped for their duties and adequate hoisting machinery must be installed.

Sound mining practice requires that ore sufficient to supply the mill for two years or more should be developed before production is begun, so that milling once started should be secure against interruption. Progress in the creation of an adequate initial ore reserve will depend to a large extent on the character of the ground, the incidence of dykes and faults, and the percentage of payability in development. In this work at least £100,000 will be required—the cost may well be a great deal more. Reduction works to deal with a monthly tonnage of 50,000 will involve another £300,000 to £400,000 and then there will be the outlay on all the other essentials such as workshops, offices, quarters for white employees and compounds for natives.

Yet another important capital item is the sum paid for the mining claims, which may run into big figures; vendors have large ideas as to the value of their property.

Nor must a company be denuded of its capital, for, with the risks inevitably associated with mining enterprise, there may be many demands that cannot be foreseen. Thus the capital scheme must make provision for all these requirements, in addition of course to what the State may demand in the way of taxation, and the interests of shareholders will demand that the profits be adequate not only for the special risks of mining but also for the repayment of the capital over the life of the mine. With a successful enterprise that may be many decades.

In view of all the risks and hazards to be faced, confidence to a notable degree is reposed in reputable mining administration on the Rand, a striking tribute to caution in judgment, soundness in method and efficiency in organization.

There are of course two sides to mining development, that on the property and that on the share market. If market operations are showing a good percentage of payability it may be unwise to see what percentage of payability there is underfoot. Many a 'good' mine, say the cynics, has been brought to ruin by sinking a shaft, and perhaps it may profit a company more to be sure of its market than to be sure of its ground.

VII

The Interdependence of Industry—Coal and Power—Big Industrial Developments

The Witwatersrand presents no more convincing example of the interdependence of industry than that of the gold mines, the collieries, and the power stations. As we have seen, an early impetus to gold mining was given by the chance discovery of coal in the Boksburg district followed by other discoveries farther east. For many years coal supplies were drawn from these areas and then with the expansion of gold mining big collieries were opened up in the Eastern Transvaal and these fields, with their superior product, gradually absorbed the bulk of the trade. Coal production in the Transvaal has reached about 8,000,000 tons (of 2000 lb.) a year. In the collieries, as in the gold mines, the bulk of the physical labour is performed by natives, and the low cost of production is shown in the average figure at the pit's mouth of only 4s. 8.27d. per ton. The consumer of course pays a good deal more, for there are the costs of rail transport to markets to be met. The gold mines consume nearly two million tons yearly at a cost of about £1,250,000, and, in addition to other industrial and domestic sales, the export and bunker trades provide a big outlet for the collieries.

On the foundation of unlimited coal resources a big organization for electric power supply has been built up which has in its turn played a notable part in the development and expansion of gold mining. That industry, because of its modern equipment and scientific organization, is to an intimate degree dependent on an abundant and cheap supply of electricity and compressed air; without this great advantage, particularly in these days of mining at great depth, operations would be severely restricted. The development on a large scale of power for the mines which began about 1906 has been almost solely in the hands of the Victoria Falls and Transvaal Power Company, Ltd., in later years, however, in close co-operation with the Electricity Supply Commission, a body created by statute in 1922 for the production, distribution and supply of electricity in the Union and to co-ordinate existing undertakings so as to promote economy and efficiency in production and supply.

In electricity and compressed air the energy supplied by the power undertaking and used by the mines and associated industries reached 2,000,000,000 units (kilowatt hours) in 1935, and the demand is rapidly rising. To the uninstructed this may not convey much light, but some idea of the magnitude of the operations on these fields will be conveyed by the fact that the Witwatersrand consumption of power in

1935 was about one-seventh of the aggregate supplied by all authorized electric power undertakings in Great Britain in 1934. The energy used by the Rand mines in 1935 would have been sufficient to send an 800-ton train hauled by an electric locomotive 1666 times round the earth. Nobody perhaps would wish to do that, but it may be comforting to some to know it could be done. Another interesting comparison is that the energy used by the mines in 1935 would cover the needs of the towns of Johannesburg, Capetown, Durban and Bloemfontein for five years. To produce this energy the power undertaking consumes no less than 7000 tons of coal a day.

The demand made by the mines is continually increasing and to cope with this rapidly rising load a new generating station, which will be the greatest in South Africa and will rank with the largest in the world, is being built near Vereeniging at a cost of about £3,500,000. The construction provides for the installation of six 33,000 k.w. turbo-generators and twelve boilers, but the design will permit of future extensions until a maximum of ten generators and the necessary boiler and auxiliary plant is reached. With the completion of the Klip generating station, as the new power house has been named, the mining industry and other consumers will be served by six stations operated by the V.F.P., two (Witbank and the new Klip station) under agreement with the Electricity Supply Commission, which has financed their construction.

BIG INDUSTRIAL DEVELOPMENTS

The Union's iron and steel industry established near Pretoria at a cost of £7,500,000 is yet another great enterprise whose fortunes are largely based on the broad structure of the gold mining industry and the many subsidiary industries which it has encouraged. For iron and steel products the Witwatersrand provides a wide market and the remarkable expansion of mining has considerably enhanced the prospects of the Pretoria undertaking.

VIII

Explosion Disasters — The Braamfontein Tragedy—Leeuwdoornstad Calamity

In view of the enormous quantities of explosives used yearly on the Witwatersrand it would have been remarkably fortunate if, in their transport by railway to the fields, no disaster had occurred. There have, in fact, been two major calamities. Old residents have vivid memories of the Braamfontein explosion, which shocked Johannesburg at a time when the community was recovering from the upheaval of the Jameson Raid incidents, and then there was the comparatively recent disaster at Leeuwdoornstad, a little village in the Western Transvaal.

The Braamfontein tragedy occurred on the afternoon of February 19th, 1896. Several trucks of dynamite had been left standing for days on a siding near this station on the west of the city, exposed to the fierce rays of the summer sun. The siding was close to hundreds of houses occupied by poor whites, natives and other coloured people, and when other wagons were shunted into these dynamite trucks there was a terrific explosion which tore a chasm 250 feet long, 60 feet wide, and 30 feet deep. The trucks had been blown to pieces; the spring of one, a piece of iron six feet long, was picked up a quarter of a mile away and another fragment of iron penetrated the roof of a building three-quarters of a mile from the scene.

There was an appalling loss of life, for in the immediate neighbourhood nearly 500 dwellings were destroyed. Eighty persons killed, 700 injured, and 1500 homeless; that was the human measure of the tragedy.

As soon as the extent of the disaster was known there was a warm-hearted response to the call for relief and the funds raised reached £125,000.

The Leeuwdoornstad calamity occurred about 6 p.m. on Sunday, July 17th, 1932, and the reverberations of the explosion were heard about twelve minutes later in Johannesburg, more than 120 miles away. Centres at far greater distances also heard the reports. As a train laden with nearly 11,000 cases of gelignite was steaming into the little Western Transvaal village the whole mass exploded, due to a hot box which caused the derailment of one of the trucks. In a small farmhouse on the outskirts of the village five people were killed instantly and others were terribly injured. The driver and fireman of the train escaped unharmed; the guard was blown to atoms. Of some of the trucks only fragments remained; others were undamaged until they caught fire. The railway track for a hundred yards was completely wrecked and splinters of metal and wood were carried many miles. In Leeuwdoornstad itself every building was damaged, and trees all round were stripped of leaves and branches. It was indeed a day of sad memory for this wayside village.

In the actual work of mining there have been serious explosions, the most disastrous being that at the Langlaagte Deep on April 13th, 1897, when thirty-four lives, including eight whites, were lost; and that at Driefontein Mine in 1907 when six Europeans and fifty-four natives were killed.

The mines use 1,500,000 cases of gelignite and gelatine dynamite a year and the total annual expenditure on explosives is not far short of three million pounds. The campaign to reduce accidents in the use of explosives is relentlessly pursued and the death-rate from this cause has shown a progressive decrease in recent years, the last figure available being that for 1934, which was 0.2 per 1000 per annum.

On April 16th, 1900, when Johannesburg was still in the hands of the republican forces, there was a disastrous explosion on the premises of Thomas Begbie & Co., iron founders and engineers, which had been commandeered for shell manufacture. In this tragedy sixteen white workmen, mostly Italians, and several natives in the workshops lost their lives. About a dozen other natives were killed in the vicinity where buildings were devastated.

PART FOUR

Administration, and State Interest

I

Companies to Groups — The Brain Trust of the Industry — Functions of the Chamber of Mines

The first step taken on a large scale for the working of deep-level ground was the formation, in February 1893, by Wernher, Beit & Co. and Eckstein & Co. (who had taken a leading part in the opening up of the fields and had been closely associated with the pioneer borehole enterprise on the Village Main Reef) of a financial company, Rand Mines Ltd., with a capital of £400,000. The holdings acquired included some ground quite close to the outcrop and on these holdings ten subsidiary companies were floated. Thus came into being the system of group control, to which the expansion and development of the industry are largely due. The example of Rand Mines, at first severely criticized because of its tendency towards centralization, was however soon followed and, as it became increasingly realized that the life of the industry had been indefinitely prolonged, deep levels, and later deeper levels, became the fashion.

The formation of deep-level companies produced another development, the process of amalgamation. Older companies began to find that the areas they had originally acquired were not large enough, some owners of deep-level ground found their funds insufficient to bring their properties to production and, in general, capital costs were enormously increased by the demands of deeper mining. These and other factors, of which not the least was the great advantage of more economical working, encouraged the tendency to amalgamation and the process continued with the growth of the industry so that, in the older areas at least, the reorganization embraced most properties. Though new wine may not be put into old bottles 'lest the bottles break and the wine run out and the bottles perish', new mines could with great advantage be merged with old, and both be preserved.

The most notable example of company amalgamation, continued after the South African War, was the formation on July 1st, 1909, of Crown Mines, Ltd., representing a fusion of nine companies, the earliest of which, the Crown Reef, had started production in 1888. Crown Mines, whose area has been extended from time to time, to-day holds pride of place as the leading producer of the fields.

As almost every property was affected by amalgamation, so the group system eventually came to embrace almost every company. That it has been for their good experience has amply shown; without it there could have been little co-ordination of practice, financial difficulties might in some cases have proved insuperable, and many services now rendered by groups to member companies such as the provision of the best technical assistance and guidance in the difficult problems that arise would not perhaps have been at command except at, in many instances, prohibitive cost. Not only has the group system brought great benefits to operating companies but it is not too much to say that the opening up of new areas, particularly in these days of heavy capital commitments, has been almost necessarily dependent on the initiative of the groups with their large financial resources and their highly efficient technical organization. Latterly there has been a tendency among groups to share the risks of new mining enterprises owing to the heavy financial commitments.

The Brain Trust of the Mining Industry—so indeed might the Transvaal Chamber of Mines be described, pooling as it does the combined wisdom and experience of its constituent bodies, the gold and coal mining companies.

The Chamber was founded on October 5th, 1889, having been preceded by the Diggers Committee formed in 1887 to protect common interests. Over the groups or individual mines it has no administrative or managerial authority, but its representative standing is due to the general recognition of the value of consultation and co-operation in all matters of mutual concern.

In republican days the Chamber was largely concerned in the war against the Government policy of concessions which imposed a severe handicap on the working of the mines, and in the decades that have followed the war it has built up a fine record of achievement in stimulating the advance and promoting the general welfare of the industry. Its supreme executive is the Gold Producers Committee, composed of representatives of the mining groups, and distinctive features of its organization are the technical advisory committee, comprising the chief consulting engineers of the groups, and committees representative of the consulting mechanical and electrical engineers and metallurgists, the mine and head office secretaries, the chief buyers of the groups, and others.

The functions of the Chamber of Mines have thus been authoritatively described: 'To facilitate discussion of all matters of mutual interest, and to formulate, as far as may be feasible, a common policy in respect of such matters as employment conditions and industrial relationship, legislation and Government action, accident prevention, the minimizing of the risks of phthisis, the provision of adequate supplies of native labour and the management of certain subsidiary industries and organizations that serve the industry in general.'

If in achieving uniformity in employment conditions and in guiding policy affecting industrial relationship the Chamber also creates some degree of rigidity, it must not be overlooked that, in the result, there is greater security for the workers for the fulfilment of obligations than they would otherwise enjoy.

As scarcely a session of Parliament passes without the introduction of some legislation affecting the mines in one or more aspects, the Chamber must always be ready to speak on their behalf and to take all practicable steps to safeguard their interests. In promoting the safety of the workers by diminishing as far as is humanly possible the danger of accidents, there is need for ceaseless endeavour and unwearying vigilance and in this field outstanding success has been achieved. As a result of the 'safety-first' campaign of the Chamber's Accident Prevention Committee, which works in close association with the Department of Mines, the accident death-rate, in spite of the greater depths, increased difficulties of mining, and great expansion of employment, has been brought down from 4.24 per thousand in 1904 to 2.02 per thousand in 1935, a low record for the industry. This represented a death-roll of 599 of which falls of ground accounted for 242, exactly the same number from this cause as in 1934, when the accident death-rate was 2.11 per thousand. Compensation for injuries to employees caused by accidents arising out of and in the course of their work is dealt with by a subsidiary organization maintained by the Chamber of Mines, the Rand Mutual Assurance Company, controlled by a board of directors representing the various mining groups. All claims that arise are promptly dealt with and the fact that very few cases are referred to the courts is a testimony to the sympathy and fairness shown in dealing with them. The company tries also to mitigate the consequences of injuries by supplying, free of charge, the most competent medical, surgical and other treatment. In the war against phthisis (a subject to which reference is made elsewhere) the most gratifying success has been achieved.

The recruitment and provision of native labour for the mines is in the hands of two subsidiary organizations under the control of the Chamber, the Native Recruiting Corporation which is responsible for the supply from British South Africa, and the Witwatersrand Native Labour Association which handles the supply from the adjacent Portuguese territory of Mozambique. Some idea of the magnitude of their task is conveyed by the fact that native employees today number close on 300,000. The continuance of the industry on its present scale is dependent on their physical labour, and without this great asset the amazing expansion of operations that has taken place in the past three years would not have been possible. In relation to whites, natives are employed in the ratio of about nine to one. Their conditions of employment and the provision made for their welfare constitute the best standard in South Africa under which native workers are employed in large numbers. Monetary wage payments to native employees on the Witwatersrand mines amount to nearly £9,000,000 a year, and an interesting sidelight is the growing popularity of the voluntary system of deferred pay, under which natives who so wish may have a proportion of their wages paid to them on their return to their far-distant homes. It is a system, too, which their womenfolk may be expected to encourage. Another facility greatly appreciated by the native workers is that for the safe keeping and transmission to their homes of accumulated earnings, a service which is also rendered without charge. These remittances amount to about £400,000 yearly. The fact that natives are to-day coming to the mines voluntarily in increasing numbers is pleasing evidence of their confidence in the controlling organization and of their satisfaction with the conditions of employment.

Of the subsidiary organizations of the Chamber of Mines one of the most important is the Rand Refinery at Germiston, established in 1921 and owned and controlled by the industry. The refinery, which is the largest and best equipped in existence, deals with all the bullion for the mines and according to competent estimate its operations represent a saving to the industry of well over £100,000 a year.

In co-operation with the Government, which provided the ground, the mining industry participates largely in the work of the South African Institute for Medical Research for the establishment of which the mines were financially responsible. It is an institution with an admirable record of national and local service and its work covers a vast field extending to-day far beyond the immediate mining requirements it was designed originally to serve.

Apart from local mine provision, the mining industry in its representative capacity has quite rightly always shown a close concern for the proper treatment and care of mine hospital cases, and some years ago the Chamber of Mines provided the funds for a special wing at the Johannesburg Hospital. Recently it was decided that the mines should establish their own hospital in Johannesburg. It will be the first catering for a single industry in South Africa and one of the few industrial hospitals in the Empire. The cost of the institution will be between £100,000 and £150,000.

There are many other activities in which the industry participates in its representative capacity, but this brief survey will serve to emphasize the broad scope and outlook of its central organization.

II

The State's Interests—Fruits of Co-operation—Value of the Leasing System

The State's concern in gold mining or in mining in general is not confined, as some shareholders might imagine, to the collection of taxation, of revenue from lease properties, or of licences and fees. Apart from the administration of the mining laws, which necessarily involves a great deal of routine work, the Department of Mines is closely concerned with many vital aspects of mining. Of these undoubtedly the most important are the safety of life and limb and the safeguarding of the health of the workers. The fact that mining accidents on the Witwatersrand have been reduced to a record low level and that a remarkable degree of success has been gained in the war against miner's phthisis is due in no small part to an efficient system of inspection and to the ready co-operation of the Department of Mines in all schemes calculated to lead to an improvement in conditions. This co-operation extends far beyond the ordinary bounds of administrative routine. In all technical matters the Department stands as adviser to the Government, and the responsibility of this work has greatly increased with the wide extension of activity and with the rapidly growing direct interest of the State in mining under the leasing system.

Mention too should be made of the Geological Survey, whose work has been of the greatest value to all mining enterprise, particularly in new exploration.

The annual report of the Government Mining Engineer constitutes a notable review of mining progress in the Union and it carries a mass of statistical information of the greatest value.

With the opening up of the Far East Rand was inaugurated a system of mining leases, based on the principle that the right of mining and disposing of all precious metals is vested in the Crown. The system was devised by the former Government Mining Engineer, Sir Robert Kotze.

Owing to the cost of mining at increasing depths holders of ground found it necessary to ask for more claims than their tenure entitled them to receive, and opportunity was taken of this fact to introduce the leasing system under which the Government receives a percentage on the net profit on a sliding scale basis, the percentage varying with the ratio of profit to recovery. The Government does not share in the mining risk and is therefore unaffected by any loss on operations.

The system was launched with the flotation in 1910 of Government Gold Mining Areas (Modderfontein) Consolidated Ltd., generally known as

State Mines, which commenced production in 1914. The company shared the experience of many others in the Far East Rand area in meeting at first with poor development results, but at a time when cash resources were nearing exhaustion the tide was turned by an advance by S. B. Joel, the financial head of the controlling corporation, the Johannesburg Consolidated Investment Company Ltd., of half a million pounds for further exploration and development. It was a bold and courageous step which however Mr. Joel never had cause to regret, for the results more than justified his faith. So profitable have been the operations of the company that up to the end of 1934 it had paid in dividends £17,850,000, and to the Government as its share of profit under the lease terms £22,243,283. Assuming payments in 1935 on the same basis as in 1934, these figures would then stand at £19,600,000 and £24,635,407 respectively.

The leasing system has grown with the expansion of the Rand and of the thirty-three large producing mines to-day (1935) twelve are lease mines (wholly or in part). In the case of Government Areas the lease exempted the company from mining taxation, but this concession has not been granted in subsequent leases. In addition to their tithes to Cæsar by way of taxation, the lease mines had up to 1935 contributed to State coffers no less than £40,000,000. Twenty per cent of the State's share of lease profits goes into current revenue and the remaining 80 per cent is paid into the loan account. Little wonder that Finance Ministers are great admirers of the system.

In future the percentage of lease mines will increase steadily because in areas where deep mining is necessary the 'mynpacht' (area to which the holder of the mining rights is entitled) will definitely be insufficient in itself for profitable exploitation. This 'mynpacht' must not exceed one quarter of the mineralized portion of the land over which the mining rights are held (which quarter the holder is entitled to select) and then he is under the necessity of applying to the Government for a lease of an additional contiguous area to form a workable mining proposition.

The Government will thus to an increasing extent have a direct participation in the profits of mining and the time may not be far distant when lease mines will outnumber other producers, a revolutionary change produced by the great expansion following the suspension of the gold standard at the end of 1932.

PART FIVE

From Mining Camp to Modern City

I

Ferreira's Camp—Primitive Conditions of the Settlement—The Birth of Johannesburg

The first arrivals on the Rand lived in tents or wagons—such were the rude beginnings of Johannesburg and some of the nearby communities. Camps were established at three principal points, at Langlaagte near the site of Walker's discovery, at a central spot near the present city of Johannesburg, and a little farther to the east where Jeppestown is to-day. The camp at Langlaagte is now marked by the little village of Paarlshoop, so called because it was founded by men from Paarl (Cape); if the very influential Dutch syndicate who held the land there had succeeded in their efforts to induce President Kruger to proclaim their ground the headquarters of the Mining Department, Johannesburg, if it had been so named, would have stood a few miles farther to the west. Paarlshoop was actually surveyed before Johannesburg and is therefore the oldest township on the Reef.

The central camp grew round the wagon of Colonel Ignatius Ferreira, D.S.O., who had trekked in from the bushveld, and was known as Ferreira's camp. It was not on the site of the present township of Ferreirastown (which developed into one of the worst slum areas of the city) but on the ground now known as the Selby township, a little farther to the south. From that small settlement of fifty years ago has grown the modern city of Johannesburg.

The eastern settlement was known as Natal Camp, because there most of the diggers from that colony were grouped, and the small stream near the camp became known as Natal Spruit.

Our interest must lie chiefly in the development of Ferreira's Camp, because of its direct link with the foundation and growth of Johannesburg. When the camp was established the only postal link with the outside world was that provided by native runners to and from Pretoria, nearly forty miles distant. Heidelberg was thirty miles to the south-east and Potchefstroom eighty miles to the south-west. Until the arrival of traders, camp dwellers had perforce to make the best provision they could for food supplies; fuel was scarce because the veld was treeless, and water had to be brought from distant springs or streams. But if there was little fuel, there were many antheaps which made excellent ovens.

If life was primitive in those early days it was full of new interests, of days spent in search of claims or in opening up the reefs on claims already acquired, of evenings spent round campfires where the fortunes of the day were discussed and where newcomers were always sure of a friendly welcome, and of mornings full of new hope and planning. If the nights were cold

Johannesburg in the cradle: A picture of a section of Ferreira's Camp in 1886.

on the bleak Witwatersrand in the winter of 1886 men could, as they did, walk about with blankets over their shoulders. If they were fortunate enough to be able to command such supplies, they could stack bags of mealies round their tents and thus protect themselves against the biting winds.

On the heels of the digger and speculator came the trader and journeyman, and houses of sods and reeds, of wattle and daub, the best available construction materials, began to appear. Wood and iron buildings soon followed. The first catering enterprise was that of a Mrs. Minnaar and her two daughters of Pretoria (or was it Potchefstroom?) whose establishment consisted of a tent pitched alongside their wagon. 'Post Office, Witwatersrand' was set up in the first store, a wood and iron building brought by A. B. Edgson, a trader, from Mulder's Drift, a coaching stage on the old Pretoria road where stood one of the early country inns. The letters were kept in a small packing case and callers did their own sorting. Edgson's store became the general meeting-place, for it was here that men bought their supplies and interests in claims were bought and sold. With a canteen licence the business developed into the Central Hotel, the first hotel in the camp.

Later the Government opened a post office in a wood and iron building a little west of the site of Johannesburg's modern library, but the rapid growth of business soon made necessary a move to larger premises. When the mails came in there was always a press of diggers and others anxious for letters, and

163

the system was instituted of calling out the names and addresses from two windows, those from A to M from one and those from N to Z from the other. How lucky that was for the Abrahamses, and the Nathans, only of course that was before the big rush.

Ultimately the post office was transferred to the site opposite the present town hall. Postal facilities naturally increased with the growth of the town and district offices were established to keep pace with the rapid expansion. In recent years Johannesburg's demands have sorely taxed the accommodation of the central building and postal headquarters have now been established in a modern structure close to the city's law courts. A branch office will be maintained on the old site.

Johannesburg's first telegraph office was opened on April 26th, 1887, and the first telephone service was established on September 1st, 1894.

An amusing sidelight on postal development is that in February 1897 the town was in danger of losing its delivery service, as the Volksraad declined to vote £3000 for its continuation. The country vote was hostile: 'Our burgers have to beg and cry for a postbag and have the trouble and expense of sending great distances for their letters. The people of Johannesburg have trams and cabs and can easily go to the post office. We would rather vote money for better postal facilities for the country people.' That was the rural attitude which influenced the decision, taken in the absence in Europe of the

Postmaster General. On his return, however, he was able to convince the Volksraad of its error, and the vote was restored.

In tents or wattle and daub buildings Ferreira's Camp saw the beginning of many business ventures. There was no church building until Johannesburg itself was established, but church services were held in many strange places, in hotels, in partly constructed stores, and in carpenters' shops. The first service on the fields is believed to have been one conducted in the open air by the Rev. S. J. du Toit, Superintendent General of Education of the Republic, whose text was 'The gold of that land is good' (Gen. ii, 12).

Such were the conditions before the goldfields had been proclaimed and before the start of Johannesburg itself. On the whole the camp was very well behaved, but a multiplicity of liquor licences was introducing a disturbing factor.

Ferreira's Camp might have continued to be the focus of development had it not been discovered that the Main Reef Series ran right through the ground. On this information the Government decided that no fresh trading licences or renewals would be granted and sent commissioners in October 1886 to settle the question of the site of the township. The camp community was agitated on this point, particularly traders, who had either to acquire stands in the township to be selected or go out of business. There was an excited public meeting, rival plans were advocated and discussed, and ultimately, on a show of hands, the selection of the farm Randjeslaagte was approved. This was Government ground which formed a triangle with its base on what is now Commissioner Street and its apex on the Parktown ridge. It was an 'odd bit left out' ('uitval grond') when the surrounding farms were originally surveyed.

The creation of a township on Randjeslaagte was not free from difficulty as, though lying north of the Main Reef Series, part of the ground was actually being worked for gold, for the farm had been one of the first proclaimed. Shafts had been put down at a number of points, one on the site of the present law courts in Pritchard Street. Thus the township was first surveyed in two separate parts by Josias de Villiers, who obtained the commission by tender, the claims of the Randjeslaagte syndicate lying in between. Whether the minor reef they had traced was of any economic importance was never determined, because the Government wisely decided that the ground should be incorporated in the township and that mining operations should, therefore, be discontinued. But this area was not included by the Government in the first sale of township stands, as the negotiations with the syndicate had not been concluded. The survey was made later by Wm. H. Auret Pritchard who has lived to see Johannesburg's fifty years of amazing development. It was after him that Pritchard Street was so named. Until a few years ago this thoroughfare was the city's great rendezvous on Saturday nights, when the central portion of it was closed to vehicular traffic and the roadway had no other use than as a promenade.

The fact that the town was surveyed in three parts and not as a whole accounts for those kinks in the main central streets running north and south, for when the separate sections were surveyed their ultimate union was not contemplated.

Mr. Pritchard has recalled that in his survey he was instructed to have as many cross streets as possible. Cross streets meant corner stands and corner stands meant higher prices because of their greater trading value, which may explain why Johannesburg is the Corner City of South Africa.

There has been much controversy on the point of the origin of the city's name, and it has been strongly contended that it was derived from the second name of President Kruger. But the Under Secretary of the Department of External Affairs, South African Republic, replying on February 18th, 1896, to an inquiry from the Swiss Consulate, Pretoria, stated definitely that the town was named after Johan Rissik (who was then Acting Surveyor General and became the first Administrator of the Transvaal under Union) and Christian Johannes Joubert (head of the Republican Mines Department). This evidence from the State Archives should finally dispose of any conflict on the point.

There was no proclamation of Johannesburg as a township; it was not necessary as the law provided for proclamation only in cases of dorps (villages) laid out on privately owned ground.

According to the first notice issued by the Government on November 11th, 1886, the first sale of stands was to have been held on November 18th on leasehold of only five years. Whether the view was that the fields would be shortlived or whether the Government wanted an opportunity to review the position again in five years' time we do not know, for the first notice was almost immediately withdrawn and another notice announced that the preliminary sale would take place on December 8th. The leasehold term was to be ninety-nine years, with a monthly stand licence of 10s. To-day, as a result of the exercise of conversion rights, property is on a freehold basis. The stands were 50 feet by 50 feet except the corner plots which were 50 feet by 100 feet. The survey had provided the largest market square in South Africa, 1300 feet by 300 feet. Its eastern and western limits are to-day marked by the City Hall and the public library; all that is left of the square is the little garden between these buildings.

On December 8th, 1886, therefore, the first sale of stands was held and realized £13,000, prices ranging from about £300 for sites facing the square (for in the best South African tradition the town must surely develop from its market square) to a few shillings. Some could not be sold and were withdrawn. Sites in the neighbourhood of where the central railway station now stands were not wanted. Isolated on the veld, they were considered useless for business purposes; no one was talking of railways in those days.

THE BIRTH OF JOHANNESBURG

Thus with the proclamation of the goldfields and the establishment of the township the stage was set for the developments which were to lead to the opening up of the world's greatest goldfield and the rise of South Africa's greatest city.

II

Stages in Johannesburg's Advance—The Grant of Concessions—President Kruger Opens a Synagogue—Early Administration

The first sale of stands was soon followed by others and Johannesburg changed with surprising rapidity from a primitive mining camp into a prosperous young town with every confidence in its future. The town, as foreseen, grew round its market square, structures of brick and of wood and iron quickly taking the place of wagon shelters and tents, shacks and reed dwellings. Building went on day and night and progress was amazing considering that most materials had to be brought hundreds of miles by wagon or other road transport from the railheads of Kimberley and Ladysmith or even from more distant points.

Soon after the survey of Randjeslaagte other township areas were laid out and incorporated and in this way Johannesburg has continued to expand in the fifty years of its development, to its own glory and to the material benefit of enterprising land companies. A white population of 3000 within a year and of over 25,000 within four years, that was the rate of the mining town's advance, and in a decade Johannesburg's population was over 100,000 with whites and natives in about equal proportions.

The young town, of course, had its problems. Water was an early difficulty. To-day Johannesburg and other Reef municipal areas have an assured supply from the impounded waters of the Vaal River over forty miles away, and for their special working needs mining companies have established large catchment dams, many of them now great pleasure resorts. But pioneers had to rely on wells and springs and then on rain-water tanks.

In water supply, as in many other matters, the Boer Government found the grant of a concession the simplest way of meeting public needs, and of benefiting public revenue. The distinction of being the first concessionaire belonged to James Sive-wright (afterwards Sir James, and a Prime Minister of the Cape Colony). In December 1887 he obtained a concession 'to lay pipes through the streets of Johannesburg in order to supply the inhabitants thereof with water', and a company was formed to take over the concession. The supply was to be obtained from springs in Doornfontein.

Pioneers, however, have a recollection of a drought so severe that, in October 1895, the Waterworks Company's service failed, and whatever supplies of water were available from springs had to be distributed by watercarts round which families gathered —father with a bucket, mother with a bedroom jug, children with kitchen utensils and even mantelpiece ornaments, and the native servant 'Jim' with the old paraffin tin. The rich washed themselves in soda water—the poor could not afford such a luxury—but even supplies of soda water began to fail. Many public works were stopped, factories were closed down, and public amusement houses suffered owing to lighting difficulties. 'Tea and coffee off' was a common notice in hotels and boarding houses; one hotel proprietor announced that there would be enough tea and coffee to go round 'if most of the guests don't have any'. Rumour had it that the brewery was at a stand-still, but the beer drinker heaved a sigh of relief—and ordered another glass—when the comforting announcement was made that no such calamity had befallen; the institution had its own well which had not failed. The Government ordained a day of national prayer for rain. On the Wanderers' sports ground rocket experiments were made, but in vain, to coax rain from the clouds. This enterprise almost led to the arrest of the chairman of the Waterworks Company, S. B. Joel, who was responsible for the venture. *'Hij sleek zijn vinger in die oog van God'* ('He is sticking his finger in the eyes of God'), exclaimed a devout police constable as he watched the impious proceedings. His protest was not difficult to understand, for, in his view, God was punishing the Rand for its wickedness. Did not the Volksraad look with disfavour on proposals for locust extermination because of the conviction that the locusts had been sent by God as a punishment for sin? Even at a Bond Congress, at Robertson, Cape Colony, in June 1908

a large majority carried a resolution against compulsory legislation for the extermination of locusts.
The view was that they were sent by a Higher Power
and it was impossible, and sacrilegious to attempt, to
exterminate them. The President's directions for
prayer for rain did not meet with unanimous approval,
even from his own following. In reply to his telegraphic instructions one Dutch minister wrote to
say that there were many objectionable matters
which required rectifying before he could see his way
clear to pray for rain. He expressed his belief that
God was punishing the country for its sins, particularly the working of mine batteries on the Sabbath
Day. Before the day appointed for humiliation and
prayer showers of rain fell, bringing some measure of
relief, and the position then steadily improved.

In October 1888 a concession was granted for the
manufacture of gas. Up to this time the only provision
for street lighting was the order that every publican
had to maintain a lamp outside his premises. It has
been remarked that Johannesburg's street corners
were particularly well illuminated in those days. No
licensing court had yet been established; to sell
liquor only a certificate from the Mining Commissioner was required. At the beginning of 1890 there
was a bar for every 100 of the population and in one
ward a bar for every 50—hardy pioneers had a thirst
for other things besides gold. Two years later licensed
houses numbered over 500, one for every 60 of the
population.

The gas company was required to supply and

maintain without charge 100 lamps for street lighting, but it was unable to exploit its concession because the cost of bringing its plant by ox-wagon from Aliwal North in the Cape exhausted its funds. In 1889 a concession was granted to another company for electric lighting and in 1891 a third company took over the assets and liabilities of the first two companies. Four years later the interests and plant of this company were bought out by the local authority at heavy cost.

The first tramways were constructed by the City and Suburban Tramway Company under a concession obtained from the Government in April 1889 by Sigismund Neumann (afterwards Sir Sigismund). The concession was for the exclusive right for a period of thirty years 'to construct and work tramways by horse power'. The first lines were opened for traffic on February 24th, 1891, the material being brought from Kimberley by ox-wagon. The cost of laying the track was over £5000 a mile.

In spiritual affairs the Government was not unmindful of the welfare of the community and granted sites for places of worship. A man of rugged Christianity but ready nevertheless to show his goodwill to others, President Kruger himself came to open a synagogue in September 1892. Known as Park Synagogue, it was built near the main railway station and was demolished a few years ago when the modern railway station was built. Eager to do the right thing, the Jewish leaders presented an address in which they hailed the President's visit as 'a happy omen for our ancient creed'. Their views must have undergone some modification when they listened to his reply.

'I see most of you are Jews,' he declared. 'I have come to convert you. I know that you were the chosen people of God in the olden times and that you believe in your religion as implicitly as I believe in my own. I hope that in good time you will be brought to what I consider to be the right religion. However, I have not come to quarrel with you for your belief and only express the hope that you will not indulge in any ceremonies I don't understand and cannot appreciate.'

It was the President himself however who was to be responsible for the introduction of novelties into the proceedings, for he declined to conform to 'the new practice' of keeping one's head covered in the House of God and declared 'the church' open 'in the name of Our Lord Jesus Christ': '*Ik verklaar deze kerk nu open in de naam von onze lieve Heer Jesus Christus. Amen.*' In a letter to *The Star* on February 28th, 1905, when a controversy was raised, Dr. Hertz, then Chief Rabbi of Johannesburg, stated that he had un-impeachable testimony which left no doubt that the President did speak bareheaded, and affidavits of newspaper men and others as to the words used in formally opening the synagogue.

In Johannesburg's first year the administration was in the hands of the Mining Commissioner, Captain von Brandis, remembered with affection by

pioneers for his genial temperament, tact and ur-
banity. He needed all these qualities in the discharge
of his complex duties, which embraced the settlement
of all disputes incidental to life in a mining camp
including those arising from the jumping of claims.
Ground could be pegged if the owner failed in the
payment of the monthly licence money. The most
ambitious enterprise of this class was that undertaken when Johannesburg had shed its mining camp
atmosphere. In September 1896 Colonel Ferreira
organized an expedition which pegged at night 382
claims belonging to several companies, embracing an
area from which gold to the value of many millions
has since been produced. Unfortunately for the venture, however, the claims had not lapsed and the
pegging was not recognized.

With the rapid growth of the town came the necessity for some system of local government and in
December 1887 a Sanitary Board, nominated by
the Government with the Mining Commissioner as
chairman, took over the control. The constitution of
the Board was changed in 1890, with twelve elected
members and three Government nominees one of
whom, styled the Government Commissioner, had
charge of the purse. A Town Council with limited
powers succeeded the Sanitary Board in 1897; half
the members to be burgers of the Republic.

This was the form of control until the outbreak of
war in October 1899 when Johannesburg had grown
to a town with a population of roughly 125,000, with
about equal numbers of whites and natives. The

municipal area had expanded to nearly six square miles and the rateable value of property was about £20,000,000. Fifteen years earlier the whole area could have been bought for a few pounds, or perhaps a wagon and a span of oxen. While Johannesburg had made this remarkable advance there were thriving communities on the East and West Rand, brought into being by the extension of the mining industry.

III

The Wider Vision—Lord Milner's Contributions to Progress—Building Advances—Proclamation as a City

The true foundations of Johannesburg's civic progress were laid in the reconstruction which followed the South African War, encouraged by the wider vision which the change had brought. Though the war lasted nearly three years, from October 1899 to May 1902, the British forces entered Johannesburg on May 31st, 1900. For the seven months the administration of the town had been in the hands of such members of the Stadsraad (Town Council) and officials as had remained, and then for a year after the British occupation the military were in control. The High Commissioner, Lord Milner, who had come to the Transvaal as Administrator, restored civic authority by the appointment of a nominated Town Council in May 1901, though it was not until the November following that the bulk of the uitlanders were allowed to return; their homecoming had to await more settled conditions. Two years later an ordinance providing for an elective Town Council was passed, and in December 1903 the first elected body came into being. The only important changes since then have been in the systems of voting, in the division of wards, in the numbers of councillors, and in the extension of the municipal franchise to women.

Johannesburg takes its municipal affairs very soberly, as indeed it is required to do under the ordinance governing both local and parliamentary elections which provides that all public houses (in the ward concerned when there is a local contest but not across the road, and in the whole municipal area when there is a general election) must be closed when the polling booths are open. It is a provision based presumably on the doctrine that an elector cannot drink and think at the same time—unless he happens to be a member of a club, when he is presumed to have acquired this facility, for club liquor licences do not come within the ban. Closed public houses, therefore, are a signal to voters that it is election day, or that it is the Sabbath, for on Sundays also bars may not be open.

The officials introduced by Lord Milner reorganized the civic administration and prepared the ground for a sound financial system on which Johannesburg has securely built. One of Lord Milner's earliest acts was the appointment of a Water Supply Commission the outcome of whose work was the creation of the Rand Water Board, the body responsible for water supply to all consumers on the Reef. The Board, after long negotiation, expropriated at a cost of two and a half million pounds the assets and rights of the waterworks company established by concession in pre-war days. For a great many years Johannesburg supplies were drawn from dolomite sources and when these showed signs of failing, owing to the rapidly advancing demand, rights were obtained in 1914 to impound the waters of the Vaal River (Brown River). The great barrage constructed below Vereeniging (famous as the seat of the peace negotiations after the war) has dammed those waters for a distance of fifty miles or more, placing the Rand supplies beyond anxiety and incidentally giving Vereeniging itself the status of a South African Henley.

The tramway concession held in Johannesburg before the war was confirmed by the Imperial Government in 1902, but as it applied only to horse traction it lost much of its value when the Town Council secured the right to provide an electric system. The company's interests were bought by the Council for £150,000 and electric trams were running in Johannesburg on February 26th, 1906. In recent years, in keeping with modern development, the Council has established extensive bus services while maintaining most of its tramway system.

The rate of Johannesburg's building progress since the resettlement after the South African War was, of course, determined by the fortunes of the gold mining industry. Thus in the years immediately following there was a big expansion, encouraged by the wider and more assured outlook of the industry; many buildings of grace and distinction were constructed at that time. There was another big forward move-

ment after Union (1910), a period coinciding with
mining expansion in the rich areas of the Far East
Rand. The foundation stone of Johannesburg's fine
city hall and municipal buildings, which cost over
£400,000, was laid by the Duke of Connaught on
November 29th, 1910, and the buildings were formally opened by Earl Buxton, Governor General, on
April 7th, 1915. The erection of these buildings on
the town's public Square involved the disappearance
from the scene of a picturesque link with the country,
a link which preserved in the city of gold an essen-
tially South African atmosphere. A chronicler has
given us an early picture: 'In 1886-7 the Market
Square was one vast dusty plain, partly surrounded
by tin shanties. Towards evening and all night long
the Boer farmers, with their ox-wagons loaded with
pigs, produce and poultry, would trek in from every
quarter, encamp upon the Square, and sleep beneath
the wagons. It was a weird and imposing experience,
watching the camp-fires burning and listening to the
lowing of the cattle in the stillness of the starry night.'
In addition to their produce farmers brought in also
samples of rock for testing in the hope that their farms
would be proved to be gold bearing. And so throughout the changing scene the Market Square where the
produce market was established continued to be the
Mecca of the farmer, if not with rock samples at any
rate with his produce, until the municipal offices were
built and the business was transferred to its present
site at Newtown where, in association with the city's
live-stock yards and abattoirs, a great market for the

farming community has been built up to a value of several million pounds yearly.

In recent years the Government has not been unmindful of its obligations to the Union's key city, and Johannesburg has received a new railway station at a cost of three-quarters of a million pounds and a new post office costing nearly half a million. New magistrates' courts are being provided to meet the town's needs and there is talk too of a new jail on a new site in place of the old fort long used for that purpose, a relic of Republican days when the town's behaviour was not taken on trust. If the change is made, a sentimental link with the memory of President Kruger will be severed, for the site of the fort was his own choosing. In any sale of the fort ground, however, it is very doubtful if sentiment would play much part, for those who have become most often attached to the old institution are not likely to be in a position to participate in the bidding.

Johannesburg's suburban development, as visitors will quickly observe, has been mainly northwards, extending for many miles. This has been dictated by the advance of mining to the south as the reefs, dipping in that direction, have been followed from the line of outcrop to their present great depths. It is one explanation of the fact that the town has a serious traffic problem. The main cause is, however, the fact that the railways separate the city from the residential areas on the north and that road outlets are far too few. A bold scheme of reform is long overdue.

Like the gold mining industry, Johannesburg has had its labour troubles, and at the end of March 1919 the town was for a week in the hands of a Board of Control established by municipal employees who had gone on strike. The immediate cause of the trouble was retrenchment in the tramways department but united action was due to general discontent in the service. When conferences failed, the Strike Committee constituted a Board of Control and as chairman of the board J. T. Bain, one of the men who had been deported in 1914, exercised a virtual dictatorship. 'All communications and correspondence must, until further notice, be addressed to the Town Clerk, Johannesburg Board of Control' ran the fiat of this body which assumed control of all municipal services. Government intervention brought about a settlement in which the strikers gained most of their demands. The death of J.T. Bain seven months later removed from the stage one of the most forceful characters in the Labour movement in South Africa.

Johannesburg was proclaimed a city by provincial ordinance on September 5th, 1928, two years after its fortieth anniversary. It was official recognition of a status widely accepted, for it had been a cathedral city for some time and for many years a city in the broad, loosely applied meaning of the term. Its position as the leading town of South Africa, second only in the African Continent to Cairo, had long been established.

One of the outstanding features of Johannesburg's

progress has been the growth of its university, a natural extension from the School of Mines and Technology started in 1904 as the Transvaal Technical Institute, and the medical courses begun in 1919. The University of the Witwatersrand, supported as it is by the mining industry and by all Reef municipalities, was opened on March 1st, 1922, and to-day students number over 2000. Its creation was largely due to the remarkable prevision of Alfred Beit, a close associate of Rhodes in Kimberley and Rhodesia, and a partner in Wernher, Beit & Co., who played a leading part in placing the gold mining industry on secure foundations. Beit died in 1906, and his will contained a bequest of £200,000 for a university. It was a remarkable revelation of faith in the future.

IV

The New Johannesburg — Its Credit and Stability

With the new Witwatersrand, created by the Union's suspension of the gold standard at the end of 1932, has come into being a new Johannesburg, and its credit stands almost as high as that of the Union itself. The indefinite extension of the life of the mining industry has enormously strengthened the basis of that credit, for it is the long view that now prevails in the estimation of securities.

Into three short years the city has crowded the building progress of three decades; from a general level of from four and five storeys with only a few structures of greater height, the building skyline has been raised in those three years to the impressive standard of buildings of ten, twelve storeys and more, imposing evidence of the spectacular increase in land values. This wonderful change is not by any means confined to the city area, for in the popular suburbs towering blocks of flats dwarf the modest single and double storey dwellings which formerly held the view. Johannesburg has been rebuilding at the rate of between half a million and three-quarters of a million pounds a month in this period of transformation and there is little sign yet that the movement has spent itself. Nor has it by any means been restricted to the mother city for, particularly on the Far East Rand, the field of the greatest mining expansion, young towns have grown out of all recognition and new towns have appeared almost, as it were, overnight.

Johannesburg is to-day in every way a modern city, alert, progressive, confident, giving a bold lead to the younger Reef communities which share its progress. The rapid advance of air-mail travel has brought the city within a few days of Europe, and the wonders of the radio and long-distance telephony have placed it in intimate touch with all parts of the world.

Compared with the few acres of fifty years ago, the city has to-day a municipal area of over eighty-five square miles (roughly 55,000 acres) embracing approximately 140 townships. There are almost nine hundred miles of roads of which about five hundred are constructed. The rateable value of property and improvements is little short of £100,000,000 and the yearly budget figures have risen to over seven and a half million pounds, including both sides of the account. The municipality gives employment in its various services to nearly 5500 whites and 10,000 natives. For the agricultural community the city provides a great market, quite apart from that created by the needs of the mines. The yearly value of animals sold on the live-stock market is £2,000,000

Aerial view of the modern Johannesburg.

Photo by the Aircraft Operating Company of Africa (Pty.) Ltd., Johannesburg.

and the produce market sales are another million pounds.

There has recently been taken a census of population for May 1936, and the preliminary figures have become available. They show a total population for the Witwatersrand of over one million (whites 400,000) which far outstrips all estimates. That is the human measure of development of but half a century in an area where formerly but a few pastoralists and their flocks found sustenance, a wonderful tribute to the majesty of gold.

Appendixes

Appendix A

The wide variation in the working results of Witwatersrand gold mines is shown in the following official table of production for March 1936:

Reference No.	Name of Company	Tons Milled	Yield		Working Revenue		Working Costs		Declared Estimated Working Profit	
			Decld. Total fine ounces	Dwts. per ton milled	Decld. Revenue £	Decld. Value of Revenue per ton s. d.	Total £	Per ton milled s. d.	Total £	Per ton milled s. d.
		(1)	(2)	(3)	(4)	(5)	(6)	(7)	(8)	(9)
1	Brakpan	136,000	34,569	5.005	241,294	35 6	135,519	19 11	105,775	15 7
2	City Deep	108,000	19,690	3.647	138,457	25 7	118,952	22 0	19,505	3 7
3	Consolidated Main Reef	155,000	30,966	3.966	218,052	28 2	156,301	20 2	61,751	8 0
4	Crown Mines	361,000	85,021	4.710	598,006	33 1	326,927	18 1	271,079	15 0
5	Daggafontein	121,500	36,440	5.921	254,497	41 10	134,366	22 1	120,131	19 9
6	Durban Deep	80,000	16,427	4.107	115,594	28 11	95,754	23 11	19,840	5 0
7	East Geduld	106,000	31,811	6.002	223,440	42 2	95,049	17 11	128,391	24 3
8	E.R.P.M.	207,000	45,458	4.392	319,744	30 11	220,984	21 4	98,760	9 7
9	Geduld	103,000	27,496	5.168	193,931	37 8	73,741	14 4	120,190	23 4
10	Geldenhuis Deep	88,100	12,525	2.843	88,103	20 0	73,608	16 8	14,495	3 3
11	Govt. G.M. Areas	212,000	67,722	6.389	478,493	45 2	187,355	17 8	291,138	27 6
12	Langlaagte Estate	96,000	15,386	3.156	108,907	22 8	81,852	17 1	27,055	5 7
13	Luipaards Vlei	48,000	10,112	4.213	71,035	29 7	50,335	21 0	20,700	8 7
14	Modder B	91,000	15,623	3.387	109,882	24 2	63,449	13 11	46,433	10 3
15	Modder Deep	50,000	8,856	3.542	62,406	24 11	37,744	15 1	24,662	9 10
16	Modder East	100,000	21,059	4.181	147,982	29 7	95,130	19 0	52,852	10 7
17	New Kleinfontein	66,000	12,374	3.744	86,821	26 4	62,483	18 11	24,338	7 5
18	New Modderfontein	198,000	43,079	4.352	303,101	30 7	138,920	14 0	164,181	16 7

Reference No.	Name of Company	Tons Milled	Yield		Working Revenue		Working Costs		Declared Estimated Working Profit	
			Decld. Total fine ounces	Dwts. per ton milled	Decld. Revenue £	Decld. Value of Revenue per ton s. d.	Total £	Per ton milled s. d.	Total £	Per ton milled s. d.
19	New State Areas	123,000	38,068	6.167	268,201	43 8	114,137	18 7	154,064	25 1
20	Nigel	24,000	8,116	6.762	57,148	47 8	34,863	29 1	22,285	18 7
21	Nourse Mines	83,000	17,338	4.182	121,924	29 5	92,342	22 3	29,582	7 2
22	Randfontein	383,000	66,240	3.459	468,233	24 5	322,017	16 10	146,216	7 7
23	Rietfontein Cons.	15,100	2,461	3.174	17,286	22 10	9,277	12 3	8,009	10 7
24	Robinson Deep	103,500	26,154	5.053	183,841	35 6	105,216	20 4	78,625	15 2
25	Rose Deep	69,000	12,166	3.517	85,489	24 9	70,906	20 6	14,583	4 3
26	Simmer and Jack	105,000	23,876	4.547	167,731	31 11	115,190	21 11	52,541	10 0
27	Springs	135,300	40,942	6.052	287,654	42 6	125,570	18 7	162,084	23 11
28	Sub Nigel	52,000	40,121	15.224	280,486	107 11	87,327	33 7	193,159	74 4
29	Van Ryn Estate	63,500	9,265	2.918	65,489	20 7	51,276	16 2	14,213	4 5
30	Van Ryn Deep	105,000	20,045	3.818	141,416	26 11	93,792	17 10	47,624	9 1
31	West Rand Cons.	166,000	32,180	3.850	228,252	27 6	132,161	15 11	96,091	11 7
32	West Springs	103,500	15,189	2.935	106,619	20 7	73,610	14 3	33,009	6 4
33	Witwatersrand	89,000	13,842	3.098	98,582	22 2	85,465	19 2	13,117	3 0
34	Witwatersrand Deep	51,600	9,881	3.802	69,231	26 10	55,704	21 7	13,527	5 3
	Miscellaneous Producers		7,068							
	Total and Averages	3998100	917,566	4.535	6407327	32 1	3717322	18 7	2690005	13 6

In this Analysis, the realizable value of March Gold (before deduction of Realization Charges) has been assumed to be £7 0s. 6d. per fine ounce.

Appendix B

The effect of the suspension of the gold standard at the end of 1932 on the Witwatersrand gold mining industry is illustrated in the comparison of working results for the years 1932, 1933, 1934 and 1935. The official figures are:

Year	Tons Milled	Yield		Working Revenue		Working Costs		Declared Estimated Working Profit		Dividends
		Declared Total fine ounces	Dwts. per ton	Declared Revenue £	Declared Value of Revenue per ton s. d.	Total £	Per ton milled s. d.	Total £	Per ton milled s. d.	Total declared £
1932	34,466,750	10,987,341	6.328	46,525,453	27 0	32,755,157	19 0	13,770,296	8 0	8,378,995
1933	36,383,800	10,413,473	5.685	63,640,955	35 0	34,946,144	19 3	28,694,811	15 9	12,411,463
1934	39,139,900	9,859,679	4.996	66,978,445	34 3	37,611,123	19 3	29,367,322	15 0	14,520,212
1935	44,234,650	10,564,904	4.729	74,199,671	33 7	41,773,656	18 11	32,426,015	14 8	16,391,166

In 1932 gold was taken at the statutory valuation of, roughly, 85s. per fine ounce. In 1933 the average price obtained was 124s. 8¾d.; in 1934 it was 138s. 0.17d., and in 1935 142s. 0.835d.

195

Appendix C

Receipts of Union Government from State Gold Mining ownership and taxation:

I. *Financial year ended March 31st, 1932.*

(*a*) State Ownership (Gross)		£2,333,341	
Less: Transfer Duty paid to Transvaal Provincial Administration	£9,640		
Bewaarplaats[1] Moneys— share paid to registered owners	£39,893		
		£49,533	
			£2,283,808
(*b*) Income Tax			£1,181,877
			£3,465,685

II. *Financial year ended March 31st, 1933.*

(*a*) State Ownership (Gross)		£2,514,633	
Less: Transfer Duty	£11,699		
Bewaarplaats Moneys— (Owners' share)	£35,836		
		£47,535	
			£2,467,098
(*b*) Income Tax			£1,797,876
			£4,264,974

[1] Any place beneath which the right to mine has been vested in the Crown.

APPENDIX C

III. *Financial year ended March 31st, 1934.*

(a) State Ownership (Gross)		£4,888,588	
Less: Transfer Duty	£27,672		
Bewaarplaats Moneys			
(Owners' Share)	£62,143		
		£89,815	
			£4,798,773
(b) Income Tax		£3,746,590	
(c) Gold Mines Excess Profits			
Duty		£6,000,000	
			£9,746,590
			£14,545,363

IV. *Financial year ended March 31st, 1935.*

(a) State Ownership (Gross)		£5,056,265	
Less: Transfer Duty	£27,971		
Bewaarplaats Moneys			
(Owners' Share)	£60,071		
		£88,042	
			£4,968,223
(b) Income Tax		£4,371,225	
(c) Gold Mines Excess Profits			
Duty		£3,865,451	
			£8,236,676
			£13,204,899

Financial year ending March 31st, 1936.

To secure to the Government fifty per cent of the profits of the industry over the level existing at the time of the suspension of the gold standard at the end of 1932 (there was a shortfall of roughly £1,000,000 in 1934-5), a surtax on the normal income tax was introduced.

APPENDIX C

The total receipts from ownership and taxation for 1935-6 will, it may be estimated, be about £14,500,000.

Acknowledgments

From both technical and other aspects this publication represents a compilation from widely scattered material. To the following sources I have been mainly indebted:

Witwatersrand Mining Practice by G. A. Watermeyer and S. N. Hoffenberg (University of the Witwatersrand), published in 1932. This standard work contains also a brief history of the gold industry largely compiled from a paper read by H. H. Webb, consulting engineer to the Consolidated Gold Fields of S.A. Ltd. in June 1903, when President of the S.A. Association of Engineers. A paper by R. S. G. Stokes (member) submitted to the Institution of Mining and Metallurgy, London, on November 21st, 1935, reviewed *Recent Developments in Mining Practice on the Witwatersrand.*

Modern Metallurgical Practice on the Witwatersrand. Paper by T. K. Prentice (associate) read before the Institution of Mining and Metallurgy on April 25th, 1935. The sections in this volume dealing with gold recovery are almost wholly based on this admirable review.

Development and Trend of Rand Winding Practice. Paper by Wm. Elsdon-Dew (past president) and J. J. P. Doland (member), S. A. Institution of Engineers, July 1935.

ACKNOWLEDGMENTS

Valedictory address, David Gilmour, S. A. Association of Engineers, 1904. Extracts given in S.A. Mining and Engineering Journal, March 19th, 1921.

'Group Administration in the Gold-Mining Industry of the Witwatersrand.' Address by John Martin, director of Central Mining and Investment Corporation Ltd. and President Chamber of Mines, before economic section of British Association for the Advancement of Science, Johannesburg, August 1st, 1929.

'Aspects of the Gold-Mining Industry of the Witwatersrand.' Address delivered by John Martin before fifth quinquennial Imperial Press Conference, Johannesburg, February 25th, 1935.

Official brochures of the Transvaal Chamber of Mines and annual reports of that body.

Problems Arising out of Temperature and Humidity in Deep Mining on the Witwatersrand. Paper read by Dr. Hans Pirow, Government Mining Engineer, before Chemical, Metallurgical and Mining Society of S.A., September, 1935. Other addresses by Dr. Pirow and annual reports.

Files of *The Star* (established in October 1887), *Standard and Diggers News* and *Transvaal Advertiser*. In particular, the fortieth anniversary issue of *The Star*, September 20th, 1926, and the issue of September 5th, 1928, commemorating the proclamation of Johannesburg as a city, one of the features of which was an article by the Union Astronomer H. E. Wood, M.SC., F.R.A.S., on 'When the shores of the Reef were washed by the waves of the Ocean'.

ACKNOWLEDGMENTS

Reminiscences of pioneers, particularly those of Wm. H. Auret Pritchard (the surveyor of the central area of Johannesburg after whom Pritchard Street is named) and of John Hunter McLea, organizer and secretary of the Pioneers of the Transvaal Goldfields.

Finally I should like to express my special indebtedness to the Honourable Patrick Duncan, Union Minister of Mines, for his great kindness in writing the introduction for this volume and to Dr. Hans Pirow, the Government Mining Engineer, for invaluable assistance on many points of technical difficulty.

Index

PERSONAL

INDEX

PERSONAL—*cont.*

COMPANIES

GENERAL

INDEX

GENERAL—*cont.*

INDEX

GENERAL—*cont.*

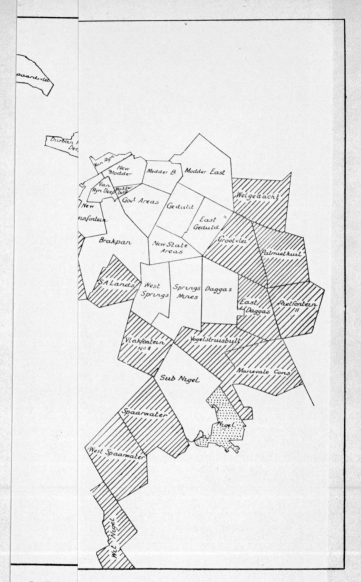

great expa The producing mines at the end of 1932.
ave started : Developing companies. Of these East
ad been la uded nor, in a map on this scale, can the
small oper *ice, Johannesburg.*

This map shows at a glance the
Dead Sea. Mines which be
Daggatnein and Groabder
may